FOUR LECTURES
ON
RELATIVITY AND SPACE

FOUR LECTURES

ON

RELATIVITY AND SPACE

BY

CHARLES PROTEUS STEINMETZ
A. M., Ph. D.

DOVER PUBLICATIONS, INC.
NEW YORK

Published in Canada by General Publishing Company, Ltd., 30 Lesmill Road, Don Mills, Toronto, Ontario.

Published in the United Kingdom by Constable and Company, Ltd., 10 Orange Street, London WC 2.

This Dover edition, first published in 1967, is an unabridged republication of the work originally published by the McGraw-Hill Book Company, Inc., in 1923.

Library of Congress Catalog Card Number: 66-30423

Manufactured in the United States of America
Dover Publications, Inc.
180 Varick Street
New York, N.Y. 10014

PREFACE

The theory of relativity developed by Einstein and his collaborators is the greatest scientific achievement of our age. The layman is therefore fully justified in wishing and asking to know what it is about and in his desire to get at least a glimpse of the new and broader conception of the universe and its laws which this theory is giving us and to understand what fundamental revolution in our scientific world conception it is causing in bringing order and system out of the previous chaotic state. Unfortunately, the relativity theory is intrinsically mathematical, and it is impossible to give a rigidly correct and complete exposition of it without the extensive use of mathematics. The best that can be done, therefore, in explaining the theory of relativity to the layman, and to the engineer who is not an expert mathematician, is to give by analogy, example and comparison a general conception of the theory and its fascinating deductions and conclusions. Such a conception must inevitably be approximate only and cannot be rigidly correct. This must become evident to the mathematical physicist. However, it is the best that can be done, and I believe it is sufficient to justify fully the little effort required from the layman to follow the exposition. After all, the non-mathematician is not interested in rigidly following the intricacies of the mathematical reasoning involved. Rather it is his desire to get a general knowledge and understanding of the new ideas on time and space, on the laws of nature and the characteristics of our universe, which the relativity theory has deduced, and of the wonderful researches into the nature of space which nearly a century ago were carried out by the great mathematicians and have now at length become of physical significance and indeed been the mathematical foundation on which the theory is built.

It is from this viewpoint that the four following lectures have been edited in order to adapt the expositions to the non-mathematical mind, even when thereby some accuracy had to be sacrificed.

The first lecture was given before the Laymen's League of the Unitarian Church of Schenectady and repeated before the Pittsfield Section of the American Institute of Electrical Engineers. The other three lectures, which go more deeply into the conclusions and deductions, and in the last lecture into the geometry of space, were also given before the Pittsfield Section of the Institute.

In conformity with the general attitude above explained, which I consider necessary to make the subject intelligible to as large a circle of readers as possible, I have introduced the constancy of the velocity of light as an axiom rather than by Michelson's experiment, and have referred to the latter only as corroboration, for the reason that in my opinion the non-technical man in search of knowledge prefers to be told the conclusions descriptively rather than to read through the record of the experimental deductions.

The derivation of Einstein's law of gravitation from the inertial motion in an accelerated system is explained by example and shown as a mathematical transformation. This gives to the layman a general understanding of the principle, but is not rigidly correct, as it gives the impression that the derivation involves no arbitrary assumptions. However, an attempt to explain general coördinates to non-technical hearers did not appear to me to be justified, and in the last lecture I tried to explain the assumptions involved in connection with the metric axiom.

Similar approximations and deviations from mathematical rigidity are found in the discussion of the imaginary unit as a quadrature vector, in relation to Minkowski's space, in the comparison of gravitational and centrifugal force, in the relation of acceleration and velocity in the derivation of the space curvature in the gravitational field, and in the explanation of the curvature of three-space by analogy with that of two-space, which obviously is limited by the conditions of the former being more complex. In a number of other places, too, the mathematical physicist will find statements and deductions which are not strictly exact, but which appeared to me justified since they appeared the only way of giving an approximate conception of a mathematical subject without mathematics.

In general I have preferred the synthetic method to the analytic as more intelligible to the non-mathematician. While most mathematicians are more familiar with the analytic method and consider it a more powerful tool, the synthetic method has in the hands of a man like Steiner proven fully as powerful as the analytic, and it has the advantage that we see what we are doing and get a physical conception of it. Thus the general or non-metric geometry is exemplified by the collinearity between the plane of points and the bundle of rays, the metric axiom is discussed, the analytical analogy of which will be obvious to the mathematicians, etc.

The entire fourth lecture has been devoted to the conception of mathematical space, its curvature, etc. This is one of the most fascinating subjects of human knowledge, and the fundamental importance which through the relativity theory it has assumed in the realm of physics makes a general understanding of it desirable for the layman, the more so as some of its conclusions—as to the finite size of the universe, etc.— have an interest reaching far beyond mathematics and physics into the realm of philosophy and beyond.

Charles P. Steinmetz.

Schenectady, N. Y.
December, 1922.

CONTENTS

CONTENTS

FOUR LECTURES ON
RELATIVITY AND SPACE

LECTURE I

GENERAL

A. RELATIVITY OF MOTION, LOCATION AND TIME

The theory of relativity as developed by Einstein and his collaborators has revolutionized science by sweeping aside many of the limitations which hitherto fettered the human intellect. But, being essentially mathematical, a general conception of it can be given to the non-mathematician only by the use of analogies and illustrations, and this inevitably involves a certain looseness of argumentation. The following pages therefore may serve to give a general idea of the theory of relativity and its consequences, but not to review it critically.

The theory of relativity starts from two premises:

1. All phenomena of space, time and motion are relative; that is, there is no absolute motion, etc., but motion, location and time have a meaning only relative to some other location, time, etc.

2. The laws of nature are universal; that is, they apply in the same form everywhere, whether in a speeding railway train on earth or in the empty space between the fixed stars.

So far, these two premises appear simple and rather obvious, but startling and revolutionary ideas appear when carrying the reasoning from these premises to their ultimate conclusions, as Einstein has done.

Suppose, for instance, you happen to run your car at 30 miles per hour against a stone wall. There seems nothing relative about this. The wreck is very real; the stone wall does not budge, and when a rapidly moving mass

1

meets an immovable body mechanical energy is set free destructively. But is the stone wall really immovable? Is it not a part of the earth, which spins around its axis at 800 miles per hour so that both the stone wall and your car were moving. And perhaps if you happened to drive the car in a westward direction—that is, against the rotation of the earth—your car really was moving more slowly than the stone wall—was going only 770 miles per hour, and the stone wall 800. But think further: Is not the stone wall, as a part of the earth, revolving around the sun at 70,000 miles per hour, and is not the sun, and with it the earth, and the stone wall, and your car, also moving on an unknown path among the fixed stars? So that really you know nothing and can know nothing about the actual or absolute speed of the car. All you know is that the relative speed of the car—that is, the speed relative to the earth and thus to the stone wall—was 30 miles per hour. But that is sufficient to let you understand the effects of the car meeting the stone wall.

So with location. The room in which you are sitting while reading appears fixed and definite. But the only way you can describe its location is by referring it to some other body or location as reference point, by saying, for instance, that your room is located x feet north and y feet west and z feet above the surveyor's markstone on City Hall Square. Or you can give its latitude, longitude and altitude, stating that from the starting point of latitude, longitude and altitude—that is, where the equator meets the zero meridian at ocean level—you go so many degrees north (or south), then so many degrees west (or east), and then so many feet up (or down), and thereby reach your room. Three distances thus are required, measured in three chosen directions, from a chosen starting point, to locate a point or an object in space, and therefore we say that space has three dimensions. But do these three distances really locate you in your room? Suppose somebody, reading the directions, should try to locate your room 1000 years hence. He would not find it. Thus one more thing must be given—the time, measured from some arbitrary starting point, for instance, anno domini. Thus, you see, to locate anything in this world of ours requires four measurements, three distances and one time; and we thus can say that the world and its events have four dimensions, three dimensions of space and one of time.

But all such location of events in the four-dimensional world can only be relative to the arbitrarily chosen reference points in space and time. In bygone ages, when people thought the earth flat and immovable as the center of the universe, they could dream of referring location to an absolute stationary reference point, say the Capitol of Rome. But when we learned that the earth is a sphere, spinning around its axis and revolving around the sun, the earth ceased to offer any fixed and permanent reference point in space. The sun then was chosen. But the astronomers found that the sun also is moving among the fixed stars. And the "fixed" stars do not stand still, but are moving "every which way," so that all the attempts to find something immovable and fixed in the universe have failed, and thus all motion, all location, can be relative only to other objects, which are also moving.

B. EFFECT OF RELATIVE MOTION ON LENGTH AND TIME

Suppose you toss a stone across your room. Observing the point at which the stone leaves your hand, the direction in which it leaves, and the speed, the physicists can calculate the path of the stone as it curves downward and finally comes to rest on the floor of the room. Suppose now you are on a railway train, moving at constant speed on a straight, level track, and toss a stone across the car in which you are riding. From the same three observations—the point in the moving railway car where the stone leaves your hand, the direction, and the speed relative to the car at which the stone leaves—the physicist by the same laws calculates the path which the tossed stone traverses in the car. Whether the car is moving at constant speed on a straight, level track or standing still makes no difference; the path of the stone is the same, as the same laws of nature apply everywhere.

If the laws of nature are the same in the railway train moving at constant speed on straight, level track as they are on the "rigid" platform of the earth or in the empty space among the fixed stars, then the speed of light must also be the same, 186,000 miles per second, and so must be the speed with which the electric current travels in its circuit, which is the speed of light. This is important because all observations depend on it. Any event is either observed by seeing it or recorded by some electrical arrangement, and in either case we do not get the exact time when the event occurs but a time later by the time it takes the light to reach our eye or the electric current to flow from the event to the recording device, and to get the exact time of the event, we therefore have to allow for the time taken by the light or the electric current. Owing to the enormous speed of the light, this time difference between the moment when the event occurs and the moment when we observe or record it usually is so extremely small as to be negligible. But not always. For instance, when on ship-board out on the ocean the chronometer has stopped and the mariner tries to find the location of his ship from the stars, he might use the eclipses of the moons of Jupiter for this purpose. But when he sees the eclipse it has already passed by from 30 to 50 minutes—depending on the relative position of the earth and Jupiter—owing to the time which it takes the light to go from Jupiter to the earth over the hundreds of millions of miles of distance.

But if the speed of light in the moving train must be the same as on the stationary track, we get some rather strange conclusions. Suppose we place a lamp on the track, back of the receding train, so that the light shines along the track (for instance, a signal light). The beam of light travels along the track at 186,000 miles per second. The train moves along the track, in the same direction, at 100 feet per second. Therefore, relative to the train, we should expect the beam of light to travel at 186,000 miles less 100 feet per second. It would be thus with a rifle bullet. If I shoot a rifle along the track at the receding train, and the rifle bullet travels along the track at 2000 feet per second, while the train travels in the same direction at 100 feet per second, then the rifle bullet will catch up with the train and pass through the train at the relative speed of 2000 less 100, or 1900, feet per second. But the constancy of the laws of nature teaches us that if the beam of light travels along the track at 186,000 miles per second, and the train in the same direction at 100 feet per second, the speed of the beam of light measured in the train (that is, its relative speed to the moving train) cannot be 186,000 miles less 100 feet, as we would expect, but must be 186,000 miles per second, the same as its relative speed to the track. Now, the only way we can explain this contradiction is to say that when we measured the speed of light on the train our measuring rods were shorter, or, using the length of the train as measure, the train was shorter, or the time was slower, or both.

These three possibilities really are one. It can be shown that if the length of the train is shorter, the time must be slower in the same proportion. Thus this leads to the strange conclusions that, when the train is moving, to the beam of light coming from the outside, and to an outside observer, the length of the train has shortened and the time in the train has slowed down. But if we now stop the train and remeasure it, we find the same length and the same time as before.

This conclusion from the two premises of the theory of relativity is so against our accustomed ideas that we would be inclined to reject it if it could not be verified by experiment, and the experiment has been made repeatedly. It is true a difference of 100 feet per second out of 186,000 miles per second is so extremely small that it could not be measured. But we can speed up the train and, instead of 100 feet per second, run it at 100,000 feet, or 20 miles, per second. We have such a train. The earth on its path around the sun moves about 20 miles per second, and the speed of light going with the motion of the earth then should be 20 miles less, going against the motion of the earth 20 miles greater. But the experiment shows that it is the same, and experiment has proven this with an accuracy many times greater than the difference in the speed of light which we should expect but do not find, so that the fact of the constancy of the speed of light is beyond question. Beyond question, then, also, is it that for an outside observer motion shortens the length and slows down the time on the moving body; but not for an observer moving with the train—for him length and time are the same.

C. RELATIVITY OF LENGTH AND DURATION

What does this mean? The train stands on the track. I measure it from the outside, you measure it from the inside, and we find the same length. We compare our watches and find them to go alike. Now the train starts and runs at high speed. While it is passing me I measure its length again and find it shorter than before, while at the same time, you, traveling with the train, measure it again from the inside and find the same length we both found when the train was standing still. But while passing over it you measure a piece of the track and find it shorter than I find it when measuring it from the outside. While you pass me on the train I compare your watch with mine and find your watch slower than mine. But, at the same time, you, comparing your watch with mine, while passing me, find *my* watch slower. Then the train stops, and both our measurements agree again. What then is the "true" length of the train and the "true" time—that which I get when measuring the train while it passes me at high speed or that which you get while moving with the train? Both, and neither. It means that length is not a fixed and invariable property of a body, but depends on the condition under which it is observed. The train has one length to the observer standing still with regard to it, that is, the observer in the train; a different and a shorter length to the observer whom it passes at 100 feet per second; and if I could go outside of the earth and measure the length of the train, while the train and earth rush by me at 20 miles per second, I would find a third still shorter length.

Length and time, therefore, are relative properties of things, depending on the conditions under which they are observed, particularly the relative speed of the body to the observer. This really is so startling only because it is novel, since at all speeds which we find around us, even the highest speeds of rifle bullets, the change of length and time is so extremely small as to be inappreciable, and we therefore are used to finding length and time constant. Appreciable changes occur only at the speed of 10,000 to 100,000 miles per second, while the most accurate methods of measurement would fail to show an appreciable shortening of the railway train going at 60 miles per hour, because the shortening is so small. But it is there just the same.

However, the relativity of the length of a body—that is, the dependence of the length on the conditions of observation—is no more strange than the relativity of the color of a body. Off-hand we will say that a body has a fixed and definite color; the grass is green, the snow is white. Nevertheless, when we think of it we know it is not so. The lady buying material for a dress in the dry-goods store during the daytime may select a nice heliotrope. But when the dress is finished, in the ballroom, she finds its color a clear soft pink. And when, to have a photograph taken, she goes to a photographer using mercury lamps in his studio, she finds the dress a clear blue. Which is its "true" color? Heliotrope, or pink, or blue? Any of the three is the true color in the condition under which it is observed.   So, Einstein's theory of relativity proves to us, it is with length and with time.   There is no single length of a body, nor time on the body, but length and time are relative and vary with the conditions under which they are observed, with the relative speed of the observer, just as the color of a body varies with the kind of light under which it is seen.

D. RELATIVITY OF MASS

If, then, in a body moving rapidly past us, the distance appears shortened and the time slowed down, the speed, which is distance divided by time, must also appear slower. Now, the energy of the moving body depends on its mass and its speed, and with the same energy put into the body, if the speed appears slower, the mass must appear larger. We thus draw the conclusion from Einstein's theory of relativity that the mass of a moving body is not constant, but increases with the speed, and the oldest of the great fundamental laws of nature, the law of conservation of matter, thus goes into the discard.   For nearly two centuries we have accepted the law of conservation of matter and believed that matter—that is, mass—can neither be created nor destroyed, and now we find that mass varies with the speed, so that speed—that is, energy—can create mass, and mass or matter probably is merely a manifestation of energy.   And this can be and has been verified experimentally.

The decrease of length, the slowing down of time, the increase of mass, becomes appreciable only at velocities approaching that of the light.   Thus at ordinary everyday velocities length, time and mass are constant; but in the vacuum tubes used in our big wireless stations to produce electrical vibrations which carry the message through space across oceans and continents, or to receive the faint signal arriving from far-distant stations, the current is carried through the empty space of the tube by minute particles, so-called electrons, and measuring the speed and the mass of these electrons, the physicists find that they move at speeds of 10,000 and 100,000 miles per second and that their mass is not constant, but increases with the speed, in the manner required by Einstein's theory. This was the first experimental proof of the change of mass, and it was found before Einstein gave the explanation in his relativity theory.

E. ACCELERATION AND THE LAW OF GRAVITATION

Suppose you have a billiard table in your house. You put a ball in the middle of the table. It stays there until something pushes it, and this something we call "force." Or you shoot a ball across the billiard table. It moves in a straight line until it strikes the boundary, rebounds and again moves in a straight line at constant speed. Suppose now we have a billiard table in a train, and the train is running at constant speed on a straight level track. You again put a ball in the middle of the table and it stays there, just as was the case in your house, at rest with regard to the table, though I, standing outside near the track, see that train and table and ball all three move together at constant speed. You shoot the ball across the table, and it moves in a straight line at constant speed, thus in the moving railway train obeying the same law of nature as in your stationary house, the law that any body keeps the same state, whether rest or motion, until something changes its state.

But suppose the train is speeding up, its speed increasing while you put the ball in the middle of the billiard table in the train. Now you find that this ball does not remain at rest, but it begins to move toward the back of the train, first slowly and then more and more rapidly until it comes to rest against the back boundary of the table, just as a stone which I drop does not remain at rest, suspended in the air, but begins to move downward with increasing speed—"falls." So the billiard ball in the speeding train "falls" toward the back of the train. You shoot a ball across the billiard table while the train is speeding up. It does not move in a straight line, but curves toward the back of the train, just as a thrown stone, on earth, does not move in a straight line at constant speed, but curves downward. You say then that in the speeding railway train some force acts on the billiard ball, pulling it toward the back of the train, just as the attraction of the earth pulls downward. You may speculate on this force which attracts things toward the back of the speeding railway train and find its laws just as Newton found the laws governing the force of gravitation. But I, standing on the embankment, near the track, while the speeding railway train passes, see that there is no real force acting on the billiard ball, but when you put it in the middle of the table, left to itself, it continues to move in a straight line at the speed which it and the train had when you put it there. What happens is that the billiard table and train, speeding up, slide forward under the ball, and the ball thus seems to fall backward toward the end of the train. So, when you shoot a ball across the billiard table in the speeding railway train, I from the outside see the ball move in a straight line at constant speed, but see billiard table and train slide forward under it, so giving you, who are moving with the speeding railway train, the impression of an attracting force pulling the ball toward the back of the train. You try to find the laws of this force; that is, the laws obeyed by the relative motion which you see. But to me these motions are those of a body left to itself, in a straight line at constant speed, and, knowing the motion of the speeding railway train, the mathematician can calculate the motion which you observe, without any physical assumption, merely as a mathematical transformation from the straight-line motion which I see from the outside to the complicated motion relative to the speeding train which you observe, and so derive the law of the latter motion—that is, the law of the fictitious attracting force—to which you ascribe these motions. This Einstein has done, and so has derived a new and more general expression for the law of gravitation, in a way which does not depend on any hypothesis concerning the nature of the force. This law is more general than Newton's law of gravitation, and the latter appears as the first approximation of Einstein's law of gravitation.

The more general law of gravitation given by Einstein does not mean that Newton's law of gravitation is wrong. Both laws give so nearly the same results in almost all cases, even in the calculation of cosmic motions, that usually the difference cannot be discovered even by the most accurate measurements. This is to say that Newton's law is a very close approximation of Einstein's. There are a few cases only in the universe as we know it today where the difference becomes noticeable. Such, for instance, is the motion of the planet Mercury. This planet has been observed for thousands of years, but all attempts to calculate its motion accurately by Newton's law have failed, while the application of Einstein's law has succeeded, thus once again corroborating his theory of relativity.

To summarize the conclusions at which we have arrived, the theory of relativity means:

All phenomena of motion, space and time are relative. The laws of nature, including the speed of light, are the same everywhere.

From these principles it follows that length, time and mass are relative also, are not fixed properties of things, but vary with the relative speed of the observer.

A more general law of gravitation is derived as a mathematical transformation of straight-line inertial motion to the apparent motion relative to a speeding system (the railway train in above illustration) and shows that gravitation is not a real force, but a manifestation of inertia, just as centrifugal force is.

LECTURE II

CONCLUSIONS FROM THE RELATIVITY THEORY

A. INTRODUCTION

The theory of relativity of Einstein and his collaborators has profoundly revolutionized our conceptions of nature. Time and space have ceased to be entities and have become mere forms of conception. The length of a body and the time on it and the mass have ceased to be fixed properties and have become dependent on the conditions of observation. The law of conservation of matter thus had to be abandoned and mass became a manifestation of energy. The law of gravitation has been recast, and the force of gravitation has become an effect of inertial motion, like centrifugal force. The ether has been abandoned, and the field of force of Faraday and Maxwell has become the fundamental conception of physics. The laws of mechanics have been changed, and time and space have been bound together in the four-dimensional world space, the dimensions of which are neither space nor time, but a symmetrical combination of both.

With such profound changes in the laws and conceptions of nature, it is startling to see that all the numerical results of calculations have remained the same. With a very few exceptions, the differences between the results of the old and of the new conceptions are so small that they usually cannot be observed even by the most accurate scientific investigation, and in the few instances where the differences have been measured, as in the disturbances of Mercury's orbit, the bending of the beam of light in the gravitational field, etc., they are close to the limits of observation.

We have seen that the length of a body and the time on it change with the relative velocity of the observer. The highest velocities which we can produce (outside of ionic velocities) are the velocity of the rifle bullet (1000 meters per second), the velocity of expansion of high-pressure steam into a vacuum (2000 meters per second), and the velocity of propagation of the detonation in high explosives (6000 meters per second). At these velocities the change of length and time is one part in 180,000 millions, 22,000 millions and 5000 millions respectively. The highest cosmic velocity probably is that of a comet passing the sun at grazing distance, 200 kilometers per second. The shortening of the length even then would be only one in four millions.

The bending of a beam of light in the gravitational field of the sun is only a fraction of a thousandth of a degree.

The overrunning of the perihelium of the planet Mercury is only about 20 miles out of more than a hundred million miles.

Therefore the principal value of the relativity theory thus far consists in the better conception of nature and its laws which it affords. Some of the most interesting illustrations of this will be discussed in the following pages.

B. THE ETHER AND THE FIELD OF FORCE

Newton's corpuscular theory of light explained radiation as a bombardment by minute particles projected at extremely high velocities, in much the same way as the alpha and the beta rays are explained today. This corpuscular theory was disproven by the phenomenon of interference, in the following manner: If the corpuscular theory is right, then two equal beams of light, when superimposed, must always combine to a beam of twice the intensity. Experience, however, shows that two equal beams of light when superimposed, may give a beam of double intensity, or may extinguish each other and give darkness, or may give anything between these two extremes. This can be explained only by assuming light to be a wave, like an alternating current. Depending on their phase relation, the combination of two waves (as two beams of light or two alternating currents) may be anything between their sum and their difference. Thus the two alternating currents consumed by two incandescent lamps add, being in phase; the two alternating currents consumed respectively by an inductance and by a capacity subtract, giving a resultant equal to their difference; that is, if they are equal, they extinguish each other. The phenomenon of interference thus leads to the wave theory of light.

If light is a wave motion, there must be something to move, and this hypothetical carrier of the light wave has been called the ether. Here our troubles begin. The phenomenon of polarization shows that light is a transverse wave; that is, the ether atoms move at right angles to the light beam, and not in its direction as is the case with sound waves. In such transverse motion a vibrating ether atom neither approaches nor recedes from the next ether atom, and the only way in which in the propagation of the light wave the vibratory motion of each ether atom can be transmitted to the next one is by forces acting between the ether atoms so as to hold them together in their relative positions. Bodies in which the atoms are held together in their relative positions are solid bodies. That is, transverse waves can exist only in solid bodies. As the velocity of light is extremely high, the forces between the ether atoms which transmit the vibrations must be very great. That is, the ether is a solid body of very high rigidity, infinitely more rigid than steel.

At the same time, the ether must be of extremely high tenuity, since all the cosmic bodies move through it at high velocities without meeting any friction. In the revolution of the earth around the sun either the ether stands still and the earth moves through the ether, at 20 miles per second, or the earth carries a mass of ether with it ("ether drift"). In the first case there should be friction between the mass of the earth and the ether; in the last case there should be friction between the ether carried along with the earth and the stationary ether. But in either case the frictional energy would come from the earth, would slow down the speed of the earth and show astronomically as a change of the orbit of the earth, and no such evidence of ether friction is observed.

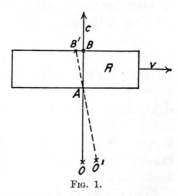

FIG. 1.

Which of the two alternative possibilities—a stationary ether or an ether moving with the earth—is true can be determined experimentally. Suppose, in Fig. 1, R is a railway train moving at speed v, and I shoot a rifle bullet through the train, in the direction at right angles to the track, at velocity c. The bullet enters the train at the point A of the track and leaves it at the point B of the track. But while the bullet passes from A to B the train has moved forward and the point B' of the train has come to the point B of the track. Thus with regard to the train—that is, for an observer in the train—the bullet moves from A to B' and thus appears to have come not from O but from O', from a direction farther forward by angle $\alpha = OAO'$, where $\tan \alpha = v/c$.

Now, instead of the train consider the earth; instead of the bullet, a beam of light from some fixed star. If, then, the ether stands still, the beam of light from a fixed star, carried by the ether, would go in a straight line $OABC$, and from the moving earth we would see the fixed star, not where it really is, at O, but deflected in the direction of the earth's motion, toward O', and a half a year later, when the earth in its orbit around the sun is moving in the opposite direction, we should see the star deflected in the opposite direction. During the annual revolution of the earth around the sun all the fixed stars thus would describe small circles. This is the case, and this phenomenon, called "aberration," proves that the ether stands still and is not carried along by the cosmic bodies.

If the ether stands still and the earth is moving through it, then by the Newtonian mechanics the velocity of light relative to the earth—that is, as observed here on earth— should in the direction of the earth's motion be 20 miles less, in the opposite direction 20 miles more, than the velocity with regard to the stationary ether. If, however, the ether moves with the earth, then obviously the velocity of light on earth should be the same in all directions. The latter is the case, and thus it is proved that the ether moves with the earth and does not stand still. This is exactly the opposite conclusion from that given by the aberration.

Thus the conception of the ether is one of those untenable hypotheses which have been made in the attempt to explain some difficulty. The more it is studied and conclusions drawn from it, the more contradictions we get, and the more unreasonable and untenable it becomes. It has been merely conservatism or lack of courage which has kept us from openly abandoning the ether hypothesis. The belief in an ether is in contradiction to the relativity theory, since this theory shows that there is no absolute position nor motion, but that all positions and motions are relative and equivalent. If, however, an ether existed, then the position at rest with regard to the ether, and the motion relative to the ether, would be absolute and different from other positions and motions, and the assumption of an ether thus leads to the conclusion of the existence of absolute motion and position and so contradicts the relativity theory.

Thus the hypothesis of the ether has been finally disproven and abandoned. There is no such thing as the ether, and light and the wireless waves are not wave motions of the ether.

What, then, is the fallacy in the wave theory of light which has led to the erroneous conception of an ether?

The phenomenon of interference proves that light is a wave, a periodic phenomenon, just like an alternating current. Thus the wave theory of light and radiation stands today as unshaken as ever. However, when this theory was established, the only waves with which people were familiar were the waves in water and the sound waves, and both are wave *motions*. As the only known waves were wave *motions*, it was natural that the light wave also was considered as a wave *motion*. This led to the question of what *moves* in the light wave, and thus to the hypothesis of the ether, with all its contradictory and illogical attributes. But there is no more reason to assume the light wave to be a wave motion than there is to assume the alternating-current wave to be a motion of matter. We know that nothing material is moving in the alternating-current or voltage wave, and if the wave theory of light had been propounded after the world had become familiar with electric waves—that is, with waves or periodic phenomena which are not wave motions of matter—the error of considering the light wave as a wave motion would never have been made and the ether theory would never have been propounded.

Hence the logical error which led to the ether theory is the assumption that a wave must necessarily be a wave motion. A wave may be a wave motion of matter, as the water wave and sound wave, or it may not be a wave motion. Electrical engineering has dealt with alternating-current and voltage waves, calculated their phenomena and applied them industrially, but has never considered that anything material moves in the alternating-current wave and has never felt the need of an ether as the hypothetical carrier of the electric wave. When Maxwell and Hertz proved the identity of the electromagnetic wave and the light wave, the natural conclusion was that light is an electromagnetic wave, that the ether was unnecessary also in optics, and, as it was illogical, to abandon it. But, curiously enough, we then began to talk about electric waves in the ether, about ether telegraphy, etc.—instead of abandoning it, that is, we dragged the conception of the ether into electrical engineering, where it never had been found necessary before.

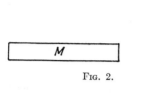

Fig. 2.

What, then, is the mechanism of the light wave and the electromagnetic wave?

Suppose we have a permanent bar magnet M (Fig. 2) and bring a piece of iron I near it. It is attracted, or moved; that is, a force is exerted on it. We bring a piece of copper near the magnet, and nothing happens. We say the space surrounding the magnet is a *magnetic field*. A *field*, or *field of force*, we define as "a condition in space exerting a force on a body susceptible to this field." Thus, a piece of iron being magnetizable—that is, susceptible to a magnetic field—will be acted upon; a piece of copper, not being magnetizable, shows no action. A field is completely defined and characterized at any point by its intensity and its direction, and in Faraday's pictorial representation of the field by the lines of force, the direction of the lines of force represents the direction of the field, and the density of the lines of force represents the intensity of the field.

To produce a field of force requires energy, and this energy is stored in the space we call the field. Thus we can go further and define the field as "*a condition of energy storage in space exerting a force on a body susceptible to this energy.*"

The space surrounding a magnet is a magnetic field. If we electrify a piece of sealing wax by rubbing it, it surrounds itself by a dielectric or electrostatic field, and bodies susceptible to electrostatic forces—such as light pieces of paper—are attracted. The earth is surrounded by a gravitational field, the lines of gravitational force issuing radially from the earth. If a stone falls to the earth, it is due to the stone being in the gravitational field of the earth and being acted upon by it.

This illustrates the difference between the conception of the field held by Faraday and Maxwell, in explaining force action, and the Newtonian theory of action at a distance. To Newton the earth is attracted by the sun and therefore revolves around it, because the force of gravitation acts across the distance between sun and earth in a manner proportional to the mass and inversely proportional to the square of the distance. To us the earth revolves around the sun because it is in the gravitational field of the sun and this field exerts a force on the earth. The force is proportional to the mass of the earth and to the intensity of the gravitational field— that is, the density of the lines of gravitational force. As the lines of force issue radially from the sun, their density decreases with the square of the distance.

Both conceptions, that of action at a distance and that of the field of force, thus give the same result and in some respects are merely different ways of looking at the same thing. But the first, the action at a distance, is logically repugnant to our ideas, as we cannot conceive how a body can act across empty space at a place where it is not and with which nothing connects it.

However, there is something more than mere logical preference in favor of the conception of the field. We may illustrate this on the magnetic field (Fig. 2). The old conception, before Faraday, was that the poles of the magnet M act across the distance on the magnet poles induced in the iron I. Accepting this action at a distance, we should expect that as long as the magnet M and the iron I remain the same and in the same relative position the force should be the same, no matter what happens elsewhere in the space which we called the magnetic field. This, however, is not the case, but the conditions existing anywhere in the field, outside of M and I, may affect and greatly

modify the action of M on I. This is difficult to explain
in a simple manner by the theory of the action at a distance, but very simple and obvious by the field theory, as
anything done anywhere in the space outside of M and I
which changes the field at I also must change the force
exerted on I. Thus a piece of iron A (Fig. 3) interposed
between M and I increases the force by concentrating the
field on I. A copper disk C inserted between I and M
(Fig. 4) as long as it is at rest has no effect, because copper
is not susceptible to the magnetic field. If, however, the
copper disk C is revolved, the force on I decreases with
increasing speed of C and finally virtually vanishes,
because electric currents induced in C screen off the field
from I. Pieces of iron, like B and C in Fig. 5, may reverse
the force exerted by M on I from an attraction to a repul-
sion by reversing the magnetic field at I.

Thus the theory of the field of force has proven simpler
and more workable than the conception of the action
at a distance, and for this reason it has been generally
accepted.

Suppose now, in Fig. 2, instead of a permanent magnet
M, we have a bundle of soft iron wires with a coil of insulated copper wire around it and send a constant direct current through the latter. We then have an electromagnet,
and the space surrounding M is a magnetic field, characterized at every point by an intensity and a direction. If
now we increase the current, the magnetic field increases;
if we decrease the current, the field decreases; if we reverse
the current, the field reverses; if we send an alternating
current through the coil, the magnetic field alternates—
that is, is a periodic phenomenon or a wave, an alternating
magnetic field wave.

Similarly, by connecting an insulated conductor to a
source of voltage we produce surrounding it an electrostatic or dielectric field—a constant field if the voltage is
constant, an alternating dielectric field—that is, a periodic
or wave phenomenon—if we use an alternating voltage.

Magnetic and dielectric fields are usually combined, since where there is a current producing a magnetic field there is a voltage producing a dielectric field. Thus the space surrounding a conductor carrying an electric current is an electromagnetic field—that is, a combination of a magnetic field, concentric with the conductor, and a dielectric field, ·radial to the conductor.

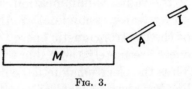

If the current and voltage are constant, the electromagnetic field is constant or stationary relative to the conductor, just as the

Fig. 3.

gravitational field of the earth is stationary with regard to the earth. If the current and voltage alternate, the electromagnetic field alternates—that is, is a periodic field or an electromagnetic wave.

Maxwell then has deduced mathematically, and Hertz demonstrated experimentally, that the alternating electromagnetic field—that is, the electromagnetic wave—has the same speed of propagation as the light wave, and has shown that the electromagnetic wave and the (polarized) light wave are identical in all their properties. Hence light is an electromagnetic wave—that is, an alternating electromagnetic field of extremely high frequency.

Electrophysics has been successfully developed to its present high state, and has dealt with alternating currents,

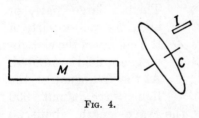

Fig. 4.

voltages and electromagnetic fields, without ever requiring or considering a medium such as the ether. Whatever may be the mechanism of the electromagnetic wave, it certainly is not a mere transverse wave motion of matter, and the light, being shown to be a high-frequency electromagnetic wave, cannot be considered any more as a wave motion of the ether. The ether thus vanishes, following the phlogiston and other antiquated physical conceptions.

The conception of the field of force, or, as we should more correctly say, the field of energy, thus takes the place of the conception of action at a distance and of the ether. The beam of light and the electromagnetic wave (like that of the radio communication station or that surrounding a power transmission line) are therefore periodic alternations of the electromagnetic energy field in space, and the differences are merely those due to the differences of frequency. Thus the electromagnetic field of the 60-cycle transmission line has a wave length of $3 \times 10^{10}/60$ cm. = 5000 km. Its extent is limited to the space between the conductors and their immediate surroundings, being therefore extremely small compared with the wave length, and under these conditions the part of the electromagnetic energy which is radiated into space is extremely small. It is so small that it may be neglected and that it may be said that all the energy supplied by the source of power which is consumed in producing the electromagnetic field is returned to the supply circuit at the disappearance of the field. In radio communication wave lengths of 15,000 to 200 meters and less—that is, frequencies of 20,000 to 1,500,000 cycles and more—are used, and the circuit is arranged so as to give the electromagnetic field the greatest possible extent, it being the field which

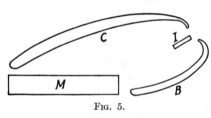

FIG. 5.

carries the message. Then a large part, or even the major part, of the energy of the electromagnetic field is radiated. At the frequency of the light wave, about 600 millions of millions of cycles, the wave length, about 50 micro cm., is an insignificant part of the extent of the field—that is, of the distance to which the beam travels—and therefore virtually all the energy of the field is radiated, none returned to the radiator.

As the electromagnetic field represents energy storage in space, it cannot extend through space instantaneously, but must propagate through space at a finite velocity, the rate at which the power radiated by the source of the field can fill up the space with the field energy. The field energy is proportional to the energy radiation of the source of the field (transmission line, radio antenna, incandescent body) and to the electromagnetic constants of space (permeability, or specific inductance, and permittivity, or specific capacity), and the velocity of propagation of the electromagnetic field—that is, the velocity of light—thus is:

$$c = \frac{1}{\sqrt{LC}} = 3 \times 10^{10} \text{ cm.,}$$

where L is the inductance, C the capacity per unit space.

As has been seen, the velocity of light has nothing to do with any rigidity and elasticity constants of matter, but is merely a function of the electromagnetic field constants of space.

Lack of familiarity with the conception of the energy field in space, and familiarity with the conception of matter as the (hypothetical) carrier of energy, may lead to the question: What is the carrier of the field energy in space? Would not the ether be needed as the hypothetical carrier of the field energy?

All that we know of the world is derived from the perceptions of our senses. They are the only real facts; all things else are conclusions from them. All sense perceptions are exclusively energy effects. That is, energy is the only real existing entity, the primary conception, which exists for us because our senses respond to it. All other conceptions are secondary, conclusions from the energy perceptions of our senses. Thus space and time and motion and matter are secondary conceptions with which our mind clothes the events of nature—that is, the hypothetical cause of our sense perceptions. Obviously, then, by carrying the explanation of light and electromagnetic waves back to the energy field—that is, to energy storage in space—we have carried it back as far as possible, to the fundamental or primary conceptions of the human mind, the perceptions of the senses, which give us the entity energy and the form under which the human mind conceives it, that of space and time.

C. THE FOUR-DIMENSIONAL TIME-SPACE OF MINKOWSKI

The relativity theory shows that length is not a constant property of a body but depends on the conditions under which it is observed. This does not mean that a body, like the railway train of our previous instance, has at some time one length, l_0, and at another time another length, l_1, but it means that at the same time the railway train has different lengths to different observers. It has the length l_0 to one observer—for instance, the observer in the railway train, who is at rest with regard to it—and at the same time a different (and shorter) length, l_1, to another observer—for instance, the observer standing near the track and watching the train passing by—and it would have still another length, l_2, to a third observer having a different relative speed with regard to the train. The same applies to the time. That is, the beat of the second-pendulum in the train has the duration t_0 to the observer in the train, and the same beat of the same second-pendulum in the train has a different (and longer) duration, t_1, to an observer on the track; and so on.

Thus the length of an object depends on the velocity of its relative motion to the observer, and as velocity is length divided by time, this makes the length of an object dependent on the time. Inversely, as the time depends on the velocity of the relative motion, the time depends on length. Thus length—that is, space dimension—and time become dependent upon each other.

We always have known that this world of ours is in reality four-dimensional—that is, every point event in the world is given by four numerical values, data, coördinates or dimensions, whatever we may call them, three dimensions in space and one dimension in time. But because in the physics before Einstein space and time were always independent of each other, we never realized this or found any object or advantage in considering the world as four-dimensional, but always considered the point events as three-dimensional in space and one-dimensional in time, treating time and space as separate and incompatible entities. The relativity theory, by interrelating space and time, thus changes our entire world conception.

The dependence of length and time on the relative velocity and thus on each other is an inevitable conclusion from the relativity theory—that is, from the two assumptions. (1) That all motion is relative, the motion of the railway train relative to the track being the same as the motion of the track relative to the train, and (2) that the laws of nature, and thus the velocity of light, are the same everywhere.

Consider, in Fig. 6; our illustration of a railway train R, moving with the velocity v, for instance, at 60 miles per

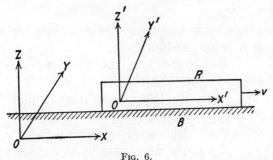

Fig. 6.

hour, relative to the track B. Let us denote the distance relative to the train—that is, measured in the train—by x', and the time in the train by t'. The distance measured along the track may be denoted by x and the time on the track by t. For simplicity we may count distance and time, in the train and on the track, from the same zero value—that is, assume $x = 0$, $t = 0$, $x' = 0$, $t' = 0$.

(This obviously makes no essential difference, but merely eliminates unnecessary constant terms in the equations of transformation from train to track and inversely.)

x' and t', the coördinates with regard to the train, thus are moving at velocity v relative to the coördinates x and t with regard to the track, and by the conventional or Newtonian mechanics, we would have:

$$t' = t,$$

that is, the time is the same on the track and in the train, and

$$x = x' + vt',$$

that is, the distance along the track x of a point of the train increases during the time t by vt', that is, with the velocity v. These equations do not apply any more in the relativity theory as they would give different velocities of light relative to the train and relative to the track. To find the equations which apply, we start with the most general relations between x, t and x', t', that is:[1]

$$x' = ax - bt,$$
$$t' = pt - qx,$$

and then determine the constants a, b, p, q by the three conditions which must be fulfilled.

1. The relative velocity of the train coördinates x', t' with regard to the track x, t *is v.*

2. By the relativity theory, the relative motion of the track with regard to the train is the same as the relative motion of the train with regard to the track; that is, x', t' are related to x, t by the same equations as x, t are related to x', t'.

3. The velocity of light c on the track, in the x, t coördinates, is the same as in the train, in the x', t' coördinates.

These three conditions give four equations between the four constants a, b, p, q, and thereby determine these constants and give, as the relations between the coördinates

---

[1] The relation must be linear, as it is univalent.

of events (that is, a material point and a time moment) relative to the moving train, x' and t', and the coördinates relative to the track, x, t, the equations:[1]

[1] In the most general expressions the train coördinates x', t' are related to the track coördinates x, t by the coördinate transformation equations:

$$\left. \begin{array}{l} x' = ax - bt \\ t' = pt - qx \end{array} \right\} \qquad (a)$$

(These equations must be linear, as one point of the train can correspond to one point of the track only, and inversely.)

1. Since $x't'$ has relative to xt the velocity v, it is, for $x' = 0: ax - bt = 0$, and since $x/t = v$, it follows:

$$\left. \begin{array}{l} b/a = v \\ b = av \end{array} \right\} \qquad (b)$$

Thus:

$$\left. \begin{array}{l} x' = ax - avt \\ t' = pt - qx \end{array} \right\} \qquad (c)$$

2. From the conditions of relativity it follows from equation (c):

$$\left. \begin{array}{l} x = ax' + avt' \\ t = pt' + qx' \end{array} \right\} \qquad (d)$$

where the reversal of the sign is obvious as the track relative to the train moves in the opposite direction to the relative motion of the train to the track:

Substituting (c) into (d) gives:

$$x(a^2 - avq - 1) + avt(p - a) = 0$$
$$t(p^2 - avq - 1) - qx(p - a) = 0$$

and as these must be identities, the coefficients of x and t must individually vanish; that is:

$$\left. \begin{array}{l} p = a \\ q = \dfrac{a^2 - 1}{av} \end{array} \right\} \qquad (e)$$

Thus, substituting into (c)

$$\left. \begin{array}{l} x' = a(x - vt) \\ t' = at - \dfrac{a^2 - 1}{av} x \end{array} \right\} \qquad (f)$$

3. From the constancy of the velocity of light it follows, that, if:

then it must be:

$$\begin{array}{l} x = ct \\ x' = ct' \end{array} \qquad (g)$$

Substituting (g) into (f) and dividing, t and t' cancel, and an equation in (d) remains, from which follows:

$$a = \frac{1}{\sqrt{1 - \dfrac{v^2}{c^2}}},$$

and by substitution into (b) and (e), the values of a, b, p and q are arrived at.

$$x' = \frac{x - vt}{\sqrt{1 - \dfrac{v^2}{c^2}}} \quad \text{or} \quad x = \frac{x' + vt'}{\sqrt{1 - \dfrac{v^2}{c^2}}} \tag{1}$$

$$t' = \frac{t - \dfrac{v}{c^2}x}{\sqrt{1 - \dfrac{v^2}{c^2}}} \quad \text{or} \quad t = \frac{t' + \dfrac{v}{c^2}x'}{\sqrt{1 - \dfrac{v^2}{c^2}}} \tag{2}$$

From these equations (1) and (2) it follows:

1. One and the same point x' of the train, at two different times, t_1' and t_2', appears as two different points of the track:

$$x_1 = \frac{x' + vt_1'}{\sqrt{1 - \dfrac{v^2}{c^2}}} \quad \text{and} \quad x_2 = \frac{x' + vt_2'}{\sqrt{1 - \dfrac{v^2}{c^2}}}$$

This is obvious and merely means that during the time interval from t_1' to t_2' the point x' of the train has moved from the point x_1 to the point x_2 of the track.

2. Two events occurring in the train at one and the same time t'—that is, simultaneously—at two different points x_1' and x_2' of the train, are not simultaneous as seen from the track, but occur at two different times:

$$t_1 = \frac{t' + \dfrac{v}{c^2}x_1'}{\sqrt{1 - \dfrac{v^2}{c^2}}} \quad \text{and} \quad t_2 = \frac{t' + \dfrac{v}{c^2}x_2'}{\sqrt{1 - \dfrac{v^2}{c^2}}}$$

and inversely.

Thus, if $x_2' > x_1'$ and the two events at x_1' and x_2' occurred not simultaneously, but the event at x_1' later than that at x_2', but by a time difference less than that between t_2 and t_1, then, seen from the track, the second event would be the later, the first one the earlier, while seen from the train the second event would be the earlier and the first one the later.

In other words, simultaneousness in time and being earlier or later in time are only relative, and two events may be simultaneous to one observer but not simultaneous to another observer because of a different relative motion; or one event may be earlier than another one to one observer and later to another observer.

3. The distance, at a given time, between two points P_1 and P_2 of the train, in train coördinates—that is, as seen from the train—is $L' = x_2' - x_1'$; in track coördinates—that is, as seen from the track—the same distance is $L = x_2 - x_1$. However, by (1):

$$x_2' - x_1' = \frac{x_2 - x_1}{\sqrt{1 - \dfrac{v^2}{c^2}}}$$

or

$$L = L'\sqrt{1 - \frac{v^2}{c^2}}$$

(3)

That is, a length L' in the train appears from the track shorter by the factor $\sqrt{1 - \dfrac{v^2}{c^2}}$ (the more, the faster the speed), and if the train were to move at the velocity of light, $v = c$, the length L' in the train would from the track appear as $L = 0$, that is, would vanish, while at a velocity greater than that of light the length L would become imaginary—that is, no velocity greater than that of light can exist.

4. The time difference between two events occurring at a point P in the train, by the time as observed by an observer in the train—that is, in train coördinates—is $T' = t_2' - t_1'$; but seen from the track—that is, for an observer watching the clock in the train while standing on the track, or in track coördinates—the time difference between the same events is $T = t_2 - t_1$. However, by (2):

$$t_2 - t_1 = \frac{t_2' - t_1'}{\sqrt{1 - \dfrac{v^2}{c^2}}}$$

or: (4)

$$T = \frac{T'}{\sqrt{1 - \dfrac{v^2}{c^2}}}.$$

That is, to the observer from the track, comparing the
clock in the train (T') with a clock on the track (T), the
clock in the train appears slow; that is, the time in the train
has slowed down by the factor .

$$\sqrt{1 - \frac{v^2}{c^2}}$$

The straight-line motion of a point (as, for instance, the
front of the railway train) can conveniently be represented
graphically by plotting the distance x as abscissa and the
time t as ordinate. A motion at constant speed then
gives a straight line for path curve, as shown by $P_0 ..P_1$ in
Fig. 7, where for convenience we chose $t = 0$ for $x = 0$. The
velocity then is given by $v_0 = \dfrac{x}{t} = \tan\ P_1 P_0 T$. An
extended body like our railway train would at time $t = 0$
be represented by a length P_0P_{00}, and at any other time

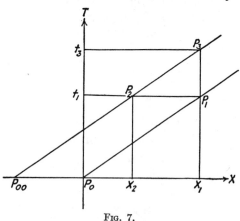

Fig. 7.

t_1 by P_1P_2 parallel to P_0P_{00}, and the motion of the train then
is represented by the area between the lines P_0P_1 —the
path curve of the front of the train—and $P_{00}P_2$—the path

curve of the back of the train. The horizontal line P_1P_2 then gives the distance $x_1 - x_2$ occupied by the train at the time t_1; that is, the length of the train is $L = x_1 - x_2$. The vertical line P_1P_3 gives the time $t_3 - t_1$ required by the train to pass a given point x_1 at velocity v_0; that is, the duration of the passage of the train is $T = t_3 - t_1$.

Now, instead of plotting the path curves of the train as in Fig. 7, with x and t as coördinates, let us plot them in the coördinates x', t' (1) and (2), as the train motion would appear to an observer having the velocity v relative to the first observer.

The equations relating $x, t,$ to $x', t',$ given by equations (1) and (2), are very similar to those representing a rotation of

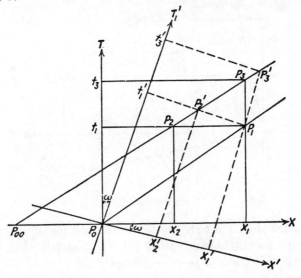

FIG. 8.

the coördinate axes by an angle $\tan \omega = v/c$. If it were such a simple rotation, the new axes X' and T' would then form with the axes X and T of Fig. 7 the angle ω, as shown in Fig. 8. For the new coördinate axes X' and T'—that is, for the observer at relative velocity v—the length of the train would be the width of the path curve parallel to X'—

that is, would be P_1P_2', instead of P_1P_2—or the length of the train would be shorter, and the duration of the passage of the train over a given point of the track would be P_1P_3' instead of P_1P_3—that is, the time would be longer.

To the second observer P_1P_2' is the train length, while to the first observer P_1P_2 is the train length and P_1P_2' not the train length but a combination of length and time. Inversely, to the second observer P_1P_2—which is the train length to the first observer—is not the train length but is a combination of length and time. Analogously, to the first observer P_1P_3 is the time of the train passage, while

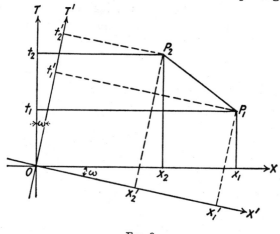

Fig. 9.

P_1P_3' is not the time but a combination of time and length. Inversely, to the second observer P_1P_3' is the time and P_1P_3 a combination of time and length.

Consider, however, two point events in the train, $x_1't_1'$ and $x_2't_2'$—that is, an occurrence at point x_1' and time t_1' and an occurrence at point x_2' and time t_2'. Then, from the track, the same two point events are given by x_1, t_1 and x_2, t_2.

Consider now these point events P_1 and P_2 represented graphically, with the distance as abscissa and the time as ordinate, as is done in Fig. 9, for both observers, at relative velocity v with each other—that is, for coördinate axes X, T and X', T' turned against each other by angle ω, where $\tan \omega = v/c$.

The distance $x_2 - x_1$ (that is, the distance between the two points as seen from the track) differs from $x_2' - x_1'$ (that is, the distance between the same two points as seen from the train), and the time $t_2 - t_1$ differs from $t_2' - t_1'$ similarly, as would be the case if x, t were one set of coördinates and x', t' a second set of coördinates, rotated with respect to the first one by angle $\tan \omega = v/c$; but the distance between the two points P_1 and P_2 obviously would be the same, whatever change of coördinates we apply; that is, it would be:

$$S^2 = (x_2 - x_1)^2 + (t_2 - t_1)^2 = (x_2' - x_1')^2 + (t_2 - t_1)^2 = S'^2$$

In the relation between the train coördinates x', t' and the track coördinates x, t, as given by equations (1) and (2), this, however, is not the case. That is, the relation between x, t and x', t', as given by equations (1) and (2)—that is, the difference of the viewpoints of the two observers—is not a simple rotation by angle ω as we have assumed above, but it is:

$$(x_2 - x_1)^2 - c^2(t_2 - t_1)^2 = (x_2' - x_1')^2 - c^2(t_2' - t_1')^2, \quad (5)$$

as easily seen from equations (1) and (2).

The appearance of the factor c^2 in equation (5) is merely due to the choice of the units of x and t.

The disadvantage, leading to complexity of equations (1) and (2), is that time and distance are given in different units, and as both equations involve both factors, they naturally would be different when given in feet and seconds from their form when given in miles and seconds, or in feet and minutes, etc., just as we would get differences and complications, in mere space relations, if, for instance, we expressed the two horizontal distances in miles and the vertical distance in feet.

The first requirement to simplify conditions is therefore to express time and distance in the same units. That is, if the distance is given in miles, express the time not in seconds, but also in miles, namely, by the distance traveled by light during the time, using the distance traveled by light in one second as the unit of time. Or, if it is desired to keep the second as unit of time, express the distance not in feet or miles, but in time measure—that is, the time required by the light to go the unit of distance. In other words, use the distance measure for time or the time measure for distance. This idea is not new. Astronomers have for long time, though for other reasons, used a time measure for large distances, the "light-year," that is, the distance traveled by light in one year.[1]

As in the world of events we have three space coördinates and one time coördinate, it is simpler to express the time in space measure—that is, to express it not in seconds (or minutes, years, etc.), but in miles, or centimeters, or whatever unit is used in the distance measurements. That is, substitute

$$w = ct \qquad (6)$$

where c is the velocity of light.

---

[1] The value of the use of time measure for the distance, or the distance measure for the time, may be very great wherever time and distance enter the same equations, and it is therefore useful in electrical engineering, for instance, when dealing with transmission line phenomena. Thus in my paper on the "General Equations of the Electric Circuit" (*A.I.E.E. Transactions*, 1907, also "Transient Phenomena," Section IV) the equations contain exponential and trigonometric functions of time t and distance l, of the form $\cos (qt \pm kl)$, etc. By choosing time measure for the distance (as more convenient in this case, since the time is the dominant term): $\lambda = \sigma l$, where $\sigma = \sqrt{LC}$ is the reciprocal of the velocity of light, the equations simplify to the form $\cos q(t \pm \lambda)$. Introducing now the local time $\vartheta = t \pm \lambda$, the complex expression of the two variables l and t simplifies into an expression of a single variable only, the "local" time ϑ; that is, the time counted at every point from the moment as starting point where the wave front reaches this point, in other words, the local time on the moving wave.

The transformation equations between train and track then become:

$$x' = \frac{x - \frac{v}{c}w}{\sqrt{1 - \frac{v^2}{c^2}}} \quad \text{or:} \quad x = \frac{x' + \frac{v}{c}w'}{\sqrt{1 - \frac{v^2}{c^2}}} \qquad (7)$$

$$w' = \frac{w - \frac{v}{c}x}{\sqrt{1 - \frac{v^2}{c^2}}} \quad\quad w = \frac{w' + \frac{v}{c}x'}{\sqrt{1 - \frac{v^2}{c^2}}} \qquad (8)$$

where x and x' are the respective distances and w and w' the respective times in distance measure.

Then we get the relation:

$$S^2 = (x_2 - x_1)^2 - (w_2 - w_1)^2 = (x_2' - x_1')^2 - (w_2' - w_1')^2 \qquad (9)$$

This, however, is not the distance between two points with coördinates x_1, w_1 and x_2, w_2, because the expression of the distance contains the plus sign.

Now, suppose we use as time measure not the distance $w = ct$, but the imaginary value of this distance, as explained later. That is, use as time coördinate:

$$u = jct; \qquad (10)$$

hence, represent the time by the imaginary value of the distance traveled by the light during the time.

Then the transformation equations (1) and (2) between train and track become:

$$x' = \frac{x + j\frac{v}{c}u}{\sqrt{1 - \frac{v^2}{c^2}}} \quad \text{or:} \quad x = \frac{x' - j\frac{v}{c}u'}{\sqrt{1 - \frac{v^2}{c^2}}} \qquad (11)$$

$$u' = \frac{u - j\frac{v}{c}x}{\sqrt{1 - \frac{v^2}{c^2}}} \quad\quad u = \frac{u' + j\frac{v}{c}x'}{\sqrt{1 - \frac{v^2}{c^2}}} \qquad (12)$$

These are the transformation equations of a rotation of the coördinates from x, u to x', u', by an angle tan $\omega = j\,v/c$, and it is then:

$$S_2 = (x_2 - x_1)^2 + (u_2 - u_1)^2 = (x_2' - x_1')^2 + (u_2' - u_1')^2 \tag{13}$$

That is: Expressing the time by the imaginary distance unit $u = jct$, the relation between the events as seen from the observer in the train and the same events as seen from an observer on the track (or in any other relative motion) is a rotation of the coördinate system x, u by the imaginary angle $j\omega$, given by tan $\omega = v/c$, and all the expressions are symmetrical in x and in u; that is, there is no difference between the distance and the time coördinates.

To the observer in the train distance and time are separate coördinates of the phenomenon occurring in the train—that is, a phenomenon regarding which the observer is at rest; but to any observer in relative motion to the phenomenon which he observes, what appear to him as distance and as time are not the same distance and time as to the observer at rest, but are compounds of distance and time. Now, physics and engineering deal with motion, and when investigating motion we obviously cannot be at rest for every motion; and therefore what we call distance and time are not absolute and intrinsically different quantities, but are combinations of the two symmetrical coördinates x and u.

It is similar to the relation, in mere space, between horizontal and vertical directions. At a given place on earth horizontal and vertical directions are intrinsically different. But, comparing two different places on earth, the horizontal and vertical directions at one place are not the same as those at the other place, but differ by a rotation of coördinates and are related to each other by the same equations as x, u and x', u'.

In the preceding we have for simplicity considered one space direction x only. This, with the time coördinate

$u = jct$, gives us two coördinates, x and u, and thus permits graphical illustration. In the events of the general world we have three space coördinates, x, y, z, and the time coördinate t, and from the relativity theory it thus follows:

Space, as represented by three dimensions, x, y, z, and time, as represented by one dimension, t, are not separate and intrinsically different, but the world and its events are a four-dimensional system, and all point events are represented by four symmetrical coördinates: x, y, z, u.

In the special case concerning an event stationary with regard to the observer, x, y and z are the three space coördinates of the Newtonian mechanics, and $u = jct$ is the time coördinate. For every event, however, in relative motion to the observer, x, y, z and u are four symmetrical coördinates, none having a preference or difference from the other, each involving the space and the time conceptions of Newtonian mechanics.

The expression of an event in coördinates x, y, z and u differs from the expression of the same event by another observer in relative motion with regard to the first, and therefore represented by coördinates x', y', z' and u', by a rotation of the coördinate system x, y, z, u against the coördinate system x', y', z', u', in the four-dimensional manifold, by an angle $\tan \omega = j\,v/c$, where v is the relative velocity.

The distance between two point events P_1 and P_2 in the four-dimensional manifold remains the same whatever coördinate system may be used—that is, is independent of the relative velocity of the observer.

$$S^2 = (x_2 - x_1)^2 + (y_2 - y_1)^2 + (z_2 - z_1)^2 + (u_2 - u_1)^2 =$$
$$(x_2' - x_1')^2 + (y_2' - y_1')^2 + (z_2' - z_1')^2 + (u_2' - u_1')^2.$$

Thus, if we consider x, y, z as space and t as time distance, relative motion v changes the space and time distance, changes the length and duration, but the total distance S in the four-dimensional manifold remains unchanged.

This four-dimensional manifold is a Euclidean space.

The equations (6) to (9) appear simpler than those of Minkowskian space, (10) to (13), as they do not contain the imaginary unit. But the distance S—equation (9)—is not the expression of the Euclidean space, and the effect of relative velocity is not a mere rotation of the coördinate system, and thus the point events do not give the same simplicity of expression as in the Minkowskian space.

Now what does this mean, rotation by an imaginary angle? It sounds unreal and meaningless. But it is no more and no less so than rotation by a negative angle. Physically, rotation by a negative angle means rotation in opposite direction, and rotation by an imaginary angle then means rotation in quadrature direction—that is, in the direction of right angle to the positive and the negative direction.

Intrinsically, only the absolute integer number has a meaning—4 horses, 4 dollars, 4 miles. Already the fraction has no intrinsic meaning; ¼ horse, for instance, is meaningless. It acquires a meaning only by defining it as denoting a relation: ¼ dollar. So the negative number intrinsically is unreal and meaningless: −4 horses has no meaning. But we attribute to it a meaning by convention, as representing the opposite direction from the positive number. Thus −4 degrees means 4 degrees below zero temperature, when +4 means 4 degrees above zero temperature, and in this relation both are equally real. But just as the negative number means the opposite direction, so the imaginary number means the quadrature direction, and $5j$ miles north of New York is just as reasonable as −10 miles north. The latter means 10 miles in the opposite direction from the northern direction, that is, south, and the former 5 miles in the quadrature direction from the northern direction, that is, west (or east). Thus the statements: Yonkers is +15 miles, Staten Island −10 miles, Jersey City $+3j$ miles, Brooklyn $-3j$ miles north of New York, are equally real and rational. When dealing with individuals, as when dealing with horses, neither the fraction nor the negative nor the imaginary number has any meaning. When dealing with divisible quantities the fraction receives a meaning. When dealing with directional quantities of one dimension, as time, temperature, etc., the negative number acquires a meaning as denoting the opposite direction to the positive. When dealing with two-dimensional functions, as geographical location, vector representation of alternating currents, etc., the imaginary number also acquires a meaning, as denoting the quadrature direction—that is, the direction at right angles to the positive and the negative.

The only difference between the conception of the negative and the conception of the imaginary number is that we have been introduced to the negative number in school and use it in everyday life and thus have become familiar with it, while this is not the case yet with the imaginary number. But inherently the imaginary number is no more and no less unreal than the negative number.

Thus, if by a rotation by angle $+\omega$ we mean a counter-clockwise rotation, a rotation by $-\omega$ would be a clockwise rotation, like that shown in Fig. 8, and a rotation by angle $j\omega$ would be a rotation at right angles; that is (in Fig. 8), out of plane of the paper, for instance a rotation around the T axis.

If, as is done in Fig. 8, we represent the relation between the viewpoints of the two observers at relative velocity v to each other, by a rotation of the coördinates x, t into $x,' t'$ by angle ω in clockwise direction (where tan $\omega = v/c$), then we get a shortening of the length, from P_1P_2 to P_1P_2', and a slowing down of the time, from P_1P_3 to P_1P_3', as required by the equations (1) and (2) of the relativity theory. But with increasing v, and thus increasing angle ω, the length as given by the equations (1) and (2) continuously decreases and becomes zero for $v = c$, while in the clockwise rotation of Fig. 8 the length P_1P_2 decreases, reaches a minimum and then increases again. Thus Fig. 8 does not physically represent the rotation given by the equations

(1) and (2). However, if we assume as representing the relation (1) and (2) a rotation by angle $j\omega$—that is, a rotation at right angles, out of the plane of the paper, for instance around the T axis—then with increasing ω the length of the train—that is, the spoor or projection of P_1P_2 on the new plane—indefinitely decreases and finally becomes zero, just as required by the equations (1) and (2).

However, the quadrature rotation, which represents the relation between x, t and x', t', is not a rotation around the T axis, as a rotation around the T axis carries us from the X axis toward the YZ plane, while the quadrature rotation $j\omega$ carries us outside of the space coördinates x, y, z into a direction at right angles to XYZ—that is, a fourth dimension of the world space of Minkowski—and therefore cannot graphically be represented any more in the three-dimensional space manifold.

In this four-dimensional manifold of Minkowski, this world or time space, which includes symmetrically the space and the time, with x, y, z, u as coördinates, we cannot say that x, y, z are space coördinates and u the time coördinate, but all four dimensions are given in the same units, centimeters or miles, or, if we wish to use the time unit as measure, seconds; but all four dimensions are symmetrical, and each contains the space and time conceptions. Thus there is no more reason to consider x, y, z as space coördinates and u as time coördinate than there is to consider x and u as space and y and z as time coördinates, etc.

Only in the special case of an observer at rest with regard to the phenomenon does x, y, z become identical with the space coördinates, and u becomes jct, where t is the time of the Newtonian mechanics.

But as soon as the observer is in motion relative to the phenomenon his viewpoint is that of a system x', y', z', u', rotated out of the Newtonian space and time, and the distinction between space and time coördinates then vanishes.

Owing to the extremely limited range of possible velocities, we cannot get far outside of the Newtonian time space.

In other words, of the four-dimensional world space of Minkowski, only a very narrow range is accessible to us, that near to the Newtonian space within rotation of a small fraction of a degree. The viewpoint from a comet passing the sun at grazing distance at 200 km. per second would differ from the Newtonian only by a rotation into the general Minkowski space by 0.04 degree.

However, within the three-dimensional timeless space of Newton the conditions are similar. We can move in the two horizontal directions x and y to unlimited distance; but in the third dimension, the vertical z, we are limited to a very few miles, so that in the Newtonian space we are practically limited to the two horizontal dimensions, just as in the general world space we are limited to the range near the Newtonian time space.

D. MASS AND ENERGY

If a body moves with the velocity v relative to the observer, from the relativity theory it follows that the length (in the direction of motion) on the body is shortened and the time lengthened by the factor $\sqrt{1 - \dfrac{v^2}{c^2}}$, where $c =$ velocity of light in vacuum.

$$L = L'\sqrt{1 - \frac{v^2}{c^2}}$$

$$T = \frac{T'}{\sqrt{1 - \dfrac{v^2}{c^2}}}$$

For $v = c$—that is, a body moving with the velocity of light—by (3) and (4), $L = 0$ and $T = \infty$. That is, on a body moving with the velocity of light the length vanishes, becomes zero, and the time stops.

For $v > c$—that is, velocities greater than the velocity of light—length and time become imaginary. That is, such velocities cannot exist. The velocity of light thus is the greatest possible physically existing velocity, and no greater relative velocity can exist or is conceivable.

This conclusion appears at first unreasonable.

Suppose we have a body moving with a velocity 90 per cent that of light, $v_1 = 0.9c$, and a second body moving with the same velocity, but in opposite direction, $v_2 = 0.9c$. The relative velocity between these two bodies thus would be $v = v_1 + v_2 = 1.8c$, or greater than the velocity of light, we would think. However, this is not so, and the error which we have made is in adding the velocities v_1 and v_2 to get the resultant velocity. This is the law of the Newtonian or pre-Einsteinian mechanics, but does not apply any more in the relativity theory, since velocity is distance—that is, length—divided by time, and as the length varies with the velocity, the velocity v_1 for a stationary observer, is not v_1 any more for an observer moving with the velocity v_2.

Thus velocities do not add algebraically, even when in the same direction.

Suppose a body moves with the velocity v_1 relative to an observer (for instance, a railway train relative to the observer on the track), and a second body moves in the same direction relative to the first body with the velocity v_2 (for instance, I walk forward in the train with the velocity v_2). What is the resultant velocity—that is, the relative velocity of the second body with regard to the observer (for instance, my velocity relative to the observer on the track)?

A point x_1t_1 relative to the train has relative to the track, by (1) and (2), the coördinates:

$$x = \frac{x_1 + v_1t_1}{\sqrt{1 - \dfrac{v_1^2}{c^2}}}$$

$$t = \frac{t_1 + \dfrac{v_1}{c^2}x_1}{\sqrt{1 - \dfrac{v_1^2}{c^2}}}$$

If now this point moves relative to the train with the velocity v_2, it is $x_1 = v_2 t_1$, and substituting this in the preceding equations and dividing gives:

$$v = \frac{x}{t} = \frac{v_1 + v_2}{1 + \dfrac{v_1 v_2}{c^2}} \tag{14}$$

as the resultant velocity v of the two velocities v_1 and v_2.

Equation (14) thus is the law of addition of velocities by the relativity theory.

If then $v_1 = 0.9c$ and $v_2 = 0.9c$, $v = 1.8c/1.81 = 0.9945c$; that is, two velocities each 90 per cent of the velocity of light add to a resultant velocity 99.45 per cent of the velocity of light.

From (14) it follows that as long as v_1 and v_2 are less than the velocity of light c, no matter how close they approach it, their sum v also is less than c.

If one of the velocities equals the velocity of light c, then, substituting in (14), we get:

$$v = \frac{v_1 + c}{1 + \dfrac{v_1}{c}} = c.$$

That is, adding—or subtracting—any velocity v_1 to or from the velocity of light c still gives the same velocity c. This explains why in the previous instance, if a train moves at the velocity v and the light along the track at the velocity c, the velocity of light relative to the train is the combination of c and v, which is again c.

The velocity of light c thus has the characteristic that any velocity (whether less than, equal to or even greater than c) may be added to it or any velocity less than c may be subtracted from it without changing it; that is, it has the characteristic of the mathematical conception of infinity: ∞.

Therefore there can be no velocity greater than c, since whatever velocity may be added to c still leaves it unchanged at c.

The kinetic energy of a mass m, moving at velocity v, is, in the Newtonian mechanics given by:

$$E = \frac{mv^2}{2}.$$

In the relativity theory the total kinetic energy of a mass m moving at the relative velocity v is given by

$$E_0 = \frac{mc^2}{\sqrt{1 - \frac{v^2}{c^2}}}.$$

and thus becomes infinite, for $v = c$, the velocity of light.

This energy, for $v = 0$, or the mass at rest, becomes:

$$E_{00} = mc^2,$$

which may be considered as the "kinetic energy of mass," while m is a constant, similar to permeability or specific capacity.

The kinetic energy required to give a mass m the relative velocity v then is given by:

$$E = \frac{mc^2}{\sqrt{1 - \frac{v^2}{c^2}}} - mc^2.$$

This expanded into a series gives:

$$E = \frac{mv^2}{2} + \frac{3}{8}\frac{mv^4}{c^2} + \; . \; . \; . \; = \frac{mv^2}{2}\left\{1 + \frac{3}{8}\frac{v^2}{c^2} + \; . \; . \; . \right\}$$

The second term already is negligible for all velocities except those comparable with the velocity of light. The first term is the kinetic energy of the Newtonian mechanics.

Mass therefore appears as a form of energy, kinetic energy, and the "energy equivalent of mass," or the "kinetic energy of mass," is $E_{00} = mc^2$.

This is an enormous energy, almost beyond conception.

One kilogram of coal, when burned, is equivalent to about 3,400,000 kgm. (kilogram-meters) or about 10 kw.-hr. (kilowatt-hours).

The earth revolves in its orbit around the sun at about 20 miles per second; that is, about thirty times as fast as the fastest rifle bullet. Its kinetic energy, $\frac{1}{2}mv^2$, therefore is enormous; 1 kg. weight on the earth has, owing to this high velocity, the kinetic energy of 50,000,000 kgm. or about 150 kw.-hr.; that is, fifteen times as much energy as would be given as heat by the combustion of the same weight of coal. (Therefore, if the earth were stopped by a collision and its kinetic energy converted into heat, its temperature would be raised by about 500,000 deg. C.)

The kinetic energy of 1 kg. weight of matter, $E_0 = mc^2$, however, is about 9000 millions of millions of kilogram-meters—or 25 thousand million kilowatt-hours—thousands of million times larger than the energy of coal.

Estimating the total energy consumed during the year on earth for heat, light, power, etc., as about 15 millions of millions of kilowatt-hours, 600 kg., or less than two-thirds of a ton of dirt, if it could be disintegrated into energy, mc^2, would supply all the heat, light and energy demand of the whole earth for a year.

Or, the energy equivalent mc^2 of one pound of dirt would run all the factories, mills, railroads, etc., and light all the cities and villages of the United States for a month. It would supply the fuel for the biggest transatlantic liner for 300 trips from America to Europe and back. And if this energy of one pound of dirt could be let loose instantaneously, it would be equal in destructive power to over a million tons of dynamite.

LECTURE III

GRAVITATION AND THE GRAVITATIONAL FIELD

A. THE IDENTITY OF GRAVITATIONAL, CENTRIFUGAL AND INERTIAL MASS

As seen in the preceding lecture, the conception of the ether as the carrier of radiation had to be abandoned as incompatible with the theory of relativity; the conception of action at a distance is repugnant to our reasoning, and its place is taken by the conception of the field of force, or, more correctly, the energy field.

The energy field is a storage of energy in space, characterized by the property of exerting a force on any body susceptible to this energy—that is, a magnetic field on a magnetizable body, a gravitational field on a gravitational mass, etc.

Light, or, in general, radiation, is an electromagnetic wave—that is, an alternation or periodic variation of the electromagnetic field—and the difference between the alternating fields of our transmission lines, the electromagnetic waves of our radio stations, the waves of visible light and the X-rays are merely those due to the differences of frequency or wave length.

The energy field at any point of space is determined by two constants, the intensity and the direction, and the force exerted by the field on a susceptible body is proportional to the field intensity and is in the direction of the energy field.

Thus the force exerted by the *magnetic field* on a magnetic material is:

$$F = HP \qquad (1)$$

where H is the *magnetic field intensity* and P the *magnetic mass*, the same quantity which in the days of action at a distance was called the magnetic pole strength, and which is related to the magnetic flux Φ by: $\Phi = 4\pi P$.

The force exerted by an *electric field* on an electrified body is:

$$F = KQ, \tag{2}$$

where K is the *dielectric field intensity* and Q the electric mass or *electric quantity*, also called *electrostatic charge*, measured in coulombs.

The force exerted by a *gravitational field* is:

$$F = gN, \tag{3}$$

where g is the *gravitational field intensity* and N the susceptibility of the body to a gravitational field, or the *gravitational mass* of the body—often simply called the mass.

The force exerted by a *centrifugal field* is

$$F = CR, \tag{4}$$

where C is the centrifugal field intensity and R the centrifugal mass.

The force F acting on a body exerts an acceleration a and thus produces a motion, a velocity v. The acceleration produced by the force is proportional to the force and inversely proportional to the resistance of the body against being set in motion—that is, the ability of the body in taking up kinetic energy, in other words, the *inertial mass* M—which thus is defined by the equation:

$$W = Mv^2/2, \tag{5}$$

where W is the *kinetic energy* taken up by the mass M to give it the velocity v.

The acceleration produced by the force thus is:

$$a = F/M, \tag{6}$$

and, substituting in (6) the expressions of the force, in equations (1) to (4), we get:

	Force:	Acceleration:	
Magnetic field........	$F = HP$	$a = HP/M$	
Electric field..........	$F = KQ$	$a = KQ/M$	(7)
Gravitational field.....	$F = gN$	$a = gN/M$	
Centrifugal field.......	$F = CR$	$a = CR/M$	

The acceleration given to a body in a field thus is proportional to the field intensity and to the energy mass (magnetic mass, electric mass, etc.) and inversely proportional to the inertial mass of the body.

That is, if I bring into the same magnetic field H two bodies of the same mass M—that is, two bodies which would require the same kinetic energy W to be given the same velocity v—and if these two bodies have two different magnetic masses, as a piece of cast iron and a piece of wrought iron, then the accelerations a will be different and the bodies will acquire different velocities. Or, inversely, two bodies of the same magnetic mass P in the same field H, but of different inertial masses M, would have different accelerations and so would be set in motion with different velocities.

In the same manner in an electric field two identical bodies—that is, bodies of the same mass M—having different electric charges Q would have different accelerations and so acquire different velocities.

Experience, however, shows that in a gravitational field as well as in a centrifugal field all bodies have the same acceleration a and thus acquire the same velocity. That means that the gravitational mass N is the same as the inertial mass M, and the centrifugal mass R is the same as the inertial mass M, in the equations (7).

This is a startling conclusion, as the gravitational mass N is the susceptibility of the body to the action of the gravitational force, just as the magnetic mass P is the susceptibility to the action of the magnetic force and as such has nothing to do with the mass M, which is the storage capacity of the body for kinetic energy. There is no more reason why the inertial mass M should be the same as the gravitational mass N than there is that M should be the same as the magnetic mass P or the electric charge Q.

This strange identity of two inherently uncorrelated quantities, the inertial mass and the gravitational mass, usually is not realized, but in writing the equation of the kinetic energy we write:

$$W = Mv^2/2,$$

and when expressing Newton's law of gravitational force we write:

$$F = M_1M_2/l^2.$$

That is, we use the same symbol M, call it mass, and never realize that there is no reason apparent why the "mass" in Newton's law of gravitation should be the same thing as the "mass" in the equation of kinetic energy.

If thus the gravitational mass equals the inertial mass, there must be some relation between the gravitational force and the inertia of moving bodies.

B. CENTRIFUGAL FORCE AS A MANIFESTATION OF INERTIA

With regard to the centrifugal force we know this, and know that the centrifugal force is not a real force, but is merely the manifestation of the inertia in a rotating system, and it is natural, then, that the "mass," which enters into the equation of centrifugal force should be the same as the inertial mass M:

$$R = M.$$

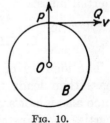

Fig. 10.

Let (in Fig. 10) B be a body revolving around a point O. The fundamental law of physics is the law of inertia.

"A body keeps the same state as long as there is no cause to change its state. That is, it remains at rest or continues the same kind of motion—that is, motion with the same velocity in the same direction—until some cause changes it, and such cause we call a 'force.'"

This is really not merely a law of physics, but it is the fundamental law of logic. It is the law of cause and effect: "Any effect must have a cause, and without cause there can be no effect." This is axiomatic and is the fundamental conception of all knowledge, because all knowledge consists in finding the cause of some effect or the effect of some cause, and therefore must presuppose that every effect has some cause, and inversely.

Applying this law of inertial motion to our revolving body in Fig. 10:

A point P of the periphery, moving with the velocity of rotation v in tangential direction, would then continue to move in the same direction, PQ, and thereby move away from the center O, first slowly, then more rapidly—that is, move in the manner in which a radial or centrifugal acceleration a acts on P, or an apparent force $F = Ma$ —by equation (6)—and this we call the centrifugal force. It is obvious, then, that all bodies would show the same centrifugal acceleration, as all would tend to move in the same manner in the same direction, unless restrained by a force (as the force of cohesion of the revolving body), and that for this reason "centrifugal mass" is identical with the inertial mass.

C. THE LAW OF GRAVITATION

The identity of the gravitational mass with the inertial mass then leads to the suspicion that the gravitational force also is not a real force, but merely a manifestation of inertia, and Einstein has shown that the laws of the gravitational force are identical with the laws of inertial motion in an accelerated system.

Let (in Fig. 11) C be a railway car standing still on a straight level track and B a billiard table in the train. I put a billiard ball A on the table, and it stands still until I push it; then it moves in a straight line at constant speed—that is, obeys the laws of inertial motion. To me in the car and to the observer on the track the behavior of the billiard ball is the same.

Suppose now (in Fig. 12) the car moves at constant velocity v on a straight level track. If I, being in the car, put a ball on the billiard table, it stands still until I push it, then

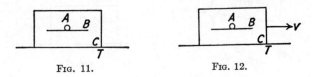

FIG. 11.   FIG. 12.

it moves at constant speed in a straight line, just as it did in Fig. 11, when the car stood still. Thus from the inside of the car I cannot distinguish whether the car is moving or standing still. The observer from the track sees the billiard ball standing still relative to the billiard table, but moving at constant speed together with the billiard table and the train. To me, in the car, and relative to the car, it seems to stand still; and when I push it its motion with reference to the observer on the track is the resultant of the motion of the ball relative to the train and the motion of the train, but still the motion is inertial motion to me in the moving car as well as to the observer on the track.

Now the car reaches a 10 per cent grade and runs up this grade at constant speed v, as shown in Fig. 13. If I now put a billiard ball on the table, it does not remain at rest, but starts moving toward the back of the train, first slowly, then with increasing velocity, and if I push the ball across the table, it does not move in a straight line, but curves backward toward the end of the train; that is, it has an acceleration due to the force acting on it. This force is a component of the force of gravity, due to the grade $p = 10$

per cent, and the acceleration thus is $a = 0.1g = 2.2$ miles per hour per second.

Suppose now, however, that the train is again running on a straight level track, not at constant speed, but at an increasing speed; that is, it is accelerating, at an acceleration $a = 2.2$ miles per hour per second, as shown in Fig. 14. If now I put a ball on the table, it does not remain at rest, but starts and moves backward with increasing velocity. If I push the billiard ball across the table, it does not run at

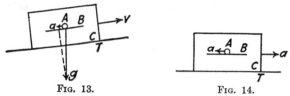

FIG. 13.   FIG. 14.

constant speed in a straight line, but curves backward, just as it did in Fig. 13 on a 10 per cent up grade at constant train speed. That is, an acceleration a, and thus apparently a force, acts on it. In short, from the inside of the car I cannot distinguish whether the train is climbing a grade at constant speed or accelerating on a level, because the effect of the acceleration of the train is identical with the effect of the force of gravitation as it acts on the billiard ball on an up grade.

To the observer from the track, however, there is a difference between the motion of the billiard ball in Fig. 13 and in Fig. 14. In Fig. 14, the observer from the track does not see any force acting on the billiard ball, and the ball moves at constant speed in a straight line, in inertial motion; but the train, and thus the billiard table, accelerating, slide forward under the ball, so that relative to the billiard table the ball seems to move with accelerated motion. Thus there is no acceleration and no force acting on the billiard ball for the observer on the track. In Fig. 13, however, on an up grade, the observer on the track notices the same acceleration acting on the billiard ball as I do in the train—that is, the same force acts on the ball relative to the observer from the track as acts on it relative to me in the train. This is obvious, since the observer on the track is in the same gravitational field.

It thus follows that the laws of inertial motion with regard to an accelerated system are the same as the laws of motion in a gravitational field. The former, however, are derived without any physical theory, merely as a mathematical transformation of the laws of inertial motion to an accelerated system. The law of gravitation thus appears here as such a mathematical transformation to an accelerated system and has been derived in this manner by Einstein.

For all velocities which are small compared with the velocity of light Einstein's law of gravitation and Newton's law give the same results, and a difference appears only when the velocity of the moving bodies approaches in magnitude the velocity of light, as is the case, for instance, with ionic motions.

Thus the gravitational field is identical with the manifestation of inertia in an accelerated system, and the law of gravitation appears as the mathematical transformation of the equation of inertial motion in fieldless space to the equation of the same motion relative to an accelerated system. The gravitational field thus is identical with an accelerated system and can be replaced by it, and, inversely, motion relative to an accelerated system can be replaced by a gravitational field.

This does not mean that any gravitational field (like that of the earth) can be replaced by some physically possible form of acceleration, but merely that the equations of motion are the same and that any limited gravitational field—for instance, that in a room—can be replaced by an acceleration in the direction of the lines of gravitational force.

The force of gravitation thus has followed the centrifugal force in being resolved into a manifestation of inertial motion, and an analogy thus exists between the centrifugal force as the (apparent) effect of the acceleration in a rotating system and the gravitational force as the effect of a rectilinear accelerating system.

If, however, gravitational force is a manifestation of inertial motion, it becomes obvious that the gravitational mass is identical with the inertial mass, just as the centrifugal mass is identical with the inertial mass.

D. CENTRIFUGAL FORCE AND GRAVITATIONAL FORCE

It is interesting to follow this analogy somewhat further. Suppose we consider a revolving body like the earth.

The equation of the centrifugal force is:

$$F_c = Ma; \qquad (8)$$

that is, mass times acceleration. Or, if v is the tangential velocity and l the radius of the revolving body:

$$F_c = Mv^2/l \qquad (9)$$

The gravitational force is in opposite direction to the centrifugal force. Thus, if we give the one the positive sign, we would give the other the negative sign. As the effect of the centrifugal force is to increase, that of the gravitational force is to decrease the distance between the acting bodies, the negative sign may be given to the latter. The gravitational force, then, is:

$$F_G = -Ma, \qquad (10)$$

that is, mass times acceleration.

We may give the gravitational force the same form by introducing a fictitious velocity v, as acceleration is of the dimension velocity square divided by length, writing:

$$F_G = -Mv^2/l \qquad (11)$$

or:

$$
\begin{aligned}
F_G &= M\left(-v^2/l\right) \\
&= M\,(jv)^2/l \\
&= Mv_0^2/\,l
\end{aligned}
\qquad (12)
$$

where $v_0 = jv$ is an imaginary velocity, and F_G then has the same equation as F_c.

Gravitation thus appears as the centrifugal force of an imaginary velocity.

An "imaginary velocity" on first sight appears unreasonable and meaningless. But it is no more so than, for instance, a negative force, as in equation (10). A "negative force" inherently has no meaning, but we give it a meaning as representing a force in opposite direction. But just as the negative sign represents the opposite direction, so the imaginary sign represents the quadrature direction. That is, an imaginary velocity is a velocity at right angles, just as a negative velocity would be a velocity in opposite direction.

As the velocity v in the equation of the centrifugal force is the tangential velocity, the imaginary velocity $v_0 = jv$ in the equation of the gravitational force is the velocity at right angles to the tangential velocity—that is, it is the radial velocity—and the gravitational force then appears as the centrifugal force of radial motion, and inversely.

Thus here, by mere mathematical formalism, we get the same relation between centrifugal and gravitational force as the effect of inertia in the acceleration due to tangential and radial motion.

E. DEFLECTION OF LIGHT IN THE GRAVITATIONAL FIELD

It is interesting to note the difference regarding the mass M between Newton's law of gravitation and Einstein's law.

In Newton's law of gravitation the mass cancels. That is, the force of gravitation is:

$$F = gM,$$

where g is the gravitational field intensity, M the mass.

The acceleration produced by the force F is:

$$a = F/M$$

and substituting for F gives:

$$a = gM/M = g.$$

The gravitational acceleration thus equals the gravitational field intensity.

In Einstein's law of gravitation the mass M does not enter at all.

Einstein's law of gravitation is the mathematical transformation of the motion of A, in Fig. 14, to an accelerated system. But whether A is a material body like a billiard ball, or a mathematical point, or an immaterial thing like a beam of light, has no effect on the mathematical equations. Neither does it make any difference whether the body A belongs to the accelerated system or enters it from the outside. For instance:

Let (in Fig. 15) R be a railway car moving at constant speed v on a straight level track, as seen from the top. I,

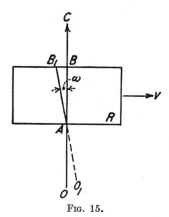

FIG. 15.

standing near the track, shoot a rifle bullet through the car, at right angles, from O to ABC. The bullet enters the car at A, in the middle of the front side. At this moment the middle of the far side of the car is at the point B in the trajectory of the bullet. When the bullet, however, reaches the far side of the car the car has moved forward, and a point B_1, back of the middle of the car, has reached the point of the track B where the bullet leaves the car. Thus, with regard to the car, the bullet moves in the direction AB_1; that is, seems to come from a point O_1, further forward. As B_1B has to AB the ratio of the velocity of the car, v, to the velocity of the bullet, v_0, the angle ω of the apparent change of the direction of the bullet is given by

$$\tan \omega = v/v_0.$$

Suppose now the car C, in Fig. 16, is not moving at constant velocity, but at increasing velocity, so that when the bullet enters the car, at A, the velocity is v_1, and when it

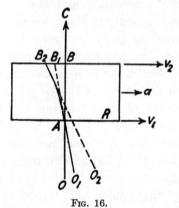

Fig. 16.

leaves the car, at the point B of the track, it is greater and is v_2. Then the angle which the bullet makes relative to the car is $\tan \omega_1 = v_1/v_0$ at the entrance of the bullet at A and is $\tan \omega_2 = v_2/v_0$ (thus being greater) when the bullet leaves the car. Thus while the bullet moves in a straight line AB relative to the track, relative to the car it curves backward, starts in the direction AB_1, as if it came from O_1, but leaves in the direction B_2O_2, as if coming from O_2. Hence it curves back just like the billiard ball in Fig. 14; that is, an acceleration and a gravitational field act on it.

Now, there obviously is no difference in the apparent motion of $OABC$ relative to the train whether it is a material body like a rifle bullet, or a mathematical point, or a beam of light. In other words:

A gravitational field acts on a beam of light in the same manner as it acts on a material body, and a beam of light in a gravitational field is deflected and curves.

A curvature necessarily means that the velocity at the inside of the curve is less than at the outside.

Thus in a gravitational field the velocity of light is not constant, nor does the light move in a straight line, but it is slowed down and deflected.

At first this seems to contradict our premise, that the velocity of light is constant and the same everywhere. However, this applied only to the velocity of light in empty space. In a material body the velocity of light is less. This follows from the phenomena of refraction. (In the same manner the velocity of propagation of electrical energy in a conductor is slowed down.) We get now a more complete understanding of the meaning of "empty space"; that is, empty space means a space free from matter and free from energy—matterless and fieldless space—and the law is: "The velocity of light in empty space, that is, in space containing no matter and no field of force, is constant, and its path a straight line, with regard to any system of reference."

Assume thus (in Fig. 16) a beam of light, of velocity c, traversing the car, while the velocity of the car increases from v_1 to v_2. The light then enters the car at the angle, relative to the car, of $\tan \omega_1 = v_1/c$, and leaves the car at the angle of $\tan \omega_2 = v_2/c$. It is deflected by the acceleration of the car—that is, by the (apparent) gravitational field existing in the car—by the angle:

$$\omega = \omega_2 - \omega_1. \tag{13}$$

As v_1 and v_2 are small compared with c, we can substitute the angle ω for $\tan \omega$; that is

$$\left. \begin{array}{l} \omega_1 = v_1/c \\ \omega_2 = v_2/c \end{array} \right\} \tag{14}$$

Thus:

$$\omega = (v_2 - v_1)/c. \tag{15}$$

If, now, t is the time required by the beam of light to traverse the car, and g the acceleration of the car, it is:

$$v_2 - v_1 = gt; \tag{16}$$

that is, the increase of velocity is acceleration times time. Substituting (16) into (15) gives:

$$\omega = gt/c \tag{17}$$

In other words, in the gravitational field of intensity g a beam of light is deflected by angle ω, which is proportional to the gravitational field intensity g, to the time t required by the light to traverse the gravitational field, and inversely proportional to the velocity of light c.

Or, in general, in a varying gravitational field, like that of the sun, the angle of deflection of a beam of light is:

$$\omega = \int \frac{gdt}{c}. \tag{18}$$

F. THE ORBIT OF THE BEAM OF LIGHT

We thus see that in a gravitational field a beam of light obeys the same laws as a material body. That is, in the gravitational field of a big mass like that of the sun a beam of light moves in the same kind of orbit as a comet or planet, the only difference in the shape of the orbit being that due to the velocity.

Thus, let (in Fig. 17) S be the sun. At a distance from the sun S a body P_1 revolves at a certain velocity. At a certain value v_1 of this velocity (about 20 miles per second at 100,000,000 miles distance) this body describes a circle (1), as the planets do approximately. If the velocity is greater, the orbit becomes elongated, taking the form of an ellipse (2), the more so the higher the velocity, until at the velocity $v_1\sqrt{2}$ the orbit becomes infinitely elongated, becoming a parabola (3), as approximated by most comets. That is, the body moves further and further away and slows down until it comes to rest at infinite distance. At still higher velocity the orbit is a hyperbola (4), and the higher the velocity the straighter the hyperbola (5) becomes, until finally, at the extremely high velocity of light, $c =$

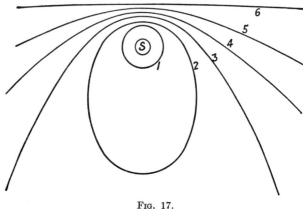

Fig. 17.

186,000 miles per second, the hyperbola (6) becomes almost a straight line. Even if the beam of light comes very close to the sun, the angle of its hyperbolic motion is only 1.7 seconds of arc, that is, about one-thousandth of the diameter of the sun. It is, however, still observable during an eclipse, by the apparent shifting of stars near the sun, when the glare of that body is cut off. Verification of the calculation has been made under this condition.

As stated above, the difference between Einstein's and Newton's laws of gravitation for velocities of the order of those of the planets and comets is so small that it cannot be observed except in a few cases, as in the motion of the planet Mercury. However, with increasing velocity, the difference increases, and it becomes 100 per cent at the velocity of light. That is, the orbit of the beam of light calculated by Newton's theory of gravitation would give only half the angle given by Einstein's theory, so that it is possible to determine by observation whether Einstein's or Newton's theory is correct. Observations during the last solar eclipses have checked with Einstein's theory of gravitation, and therefore with the relativity theory, on which it is based.

G. MATHEMATICAL EFFECTS OF GRAVITATIONAL AND CENTRIFUGAL FIELD

As has been seen, centrifugal force is the inertial effect of rotary motion, and the laws of gravitational force are identical with the inertial effect of radial acceleration. We have seen, however, in the preceding lectures, that relative motion affects the length of a body and the time on the body, shortens the length and slows down the time. Therefore, in the centrifugal field as well as in the gravitational field, mathematical effects due to the change of length by the relative motion, and physical effects due to the slowing down of time, may be expected.

Suppose we measure a flywheel, first while it is standing still. We measure its diameter and find it d, and then measure the circumference with the same measure and find it C, and we find that the circumference is π times the diameter:

$$C = \pi d. \qquad (19)$$

Now we again measure the flywheel, but while it is rapidly revolving. We stand outside and watch it spinning around while it is being measured. We find the same measure for the diameter d, because the motion of the flywheel is tangential—that is, at right angles to the direction of the measure as it is used in measuring the diameter—and the motion thus does not affect the length of the measure. But when I measure the circumference of the revolving flywheel, the motion is in the same direction in which I use the measuring rod, and the length of the measuring rod thus appears shorter to me outside of the flywheel. In other words, the measuring rod is shortened and therefore is contained in the circumference a larger number of times than before; that is, for the circumference C we get a larger number than before. Hence:

$$C > \pi d. \qquad (20)$$

As the shortening of the rod is by the factor $\sqrt{1 - \dfrac{v^2}{c^2}}$, it thus is, in the centrifugal field:

$$C = \frac{\pi d}{\sqrt{1 - \dfrac{v^2}{c^2}}}. \qquad (21)$$

Now let us do the same thing in a gravitational field, that is, a radially accelerated system. We find the circumference C to be the same as if no gravitation existed, as the acceleration is radial and thus does not affect the measuring rod used in a tangential direction in measuring the circumference. When measuring the diameter, however, the measuring rod is shortened, and the diameter thus comes out larger than it would in the absence of a gravitational field. As the circumference C has remained the same and the diameter d has increased in measure, the circumference is not πd any more, but less; that is, in a gravitational field, it is

$$C < \pi d. \qquad (22)$$

That means that in the gravitational field and in the centrifugal field the laws of mathematics are changed.

The circumference of a circle surrounding a converging gravitational field like that of the sun is less than π times the diameter. Suppose now by the laws of conventional mathematics we calculate the orbit of the planet Mercury, which is in an intense gravitational field—being nearest the sun. The actual circumference being a little shorter, owing to $C < \pi d$ in the gravitational field, in the time calculated for the orbit, the planet will make a little more than a complete orbit, overreach by about 20 miles per revolution (out of 250,000,000). This amount is small, but quite noticeable astronomically, and Newton's law of gravitation cannot account for it, but Einstein's does.

It must be realized that the change of the mathematics of space in the gravitational field is not due merely to the field intensity, but also to the configuration of the gravitational field. Thus in a convergent gravitational field, like that of the sun or the earth, the periphery of a circle surrounding the field is shortening: $C < \pi d$. In a divergent gravitational field, which would be the same as a convergent centrifugal field, the circumference of the circle is lengthened, $C < \pi d$. In a parallel gravitational field, like that of the accelerating railway car, a circle would be flattened into an ellipse; that is, the diameter parallel to the direction of the field would be different from the diameter at right angles to the field. But the relation of the circumference to the two diameters would be the same as in the ellipse of the conventional mathematics.

H. THE FINITE VOLUME OF THE UNIVERSE

All the theorems of mathematics are closely interrelated, so that if one is changed many others, and some of the axioms as well, must also be changed.

We have seen that in a gravitational field the relation between the circumference and the diameter of the circle is changed, and that the circumference is less than π times the diameter, the more so the larger the circle, and becomes equal to πd only for infinitely small circles. From this change other changes follow. Thus the sum of the angles in a triangle is not any longer equal to 180 degrees, but is greater—the more so the larger the triangle—and becomes equal to 180 degrees only in an infinitely small triangle. Another conclusion which follows is that we cannot draw a parallel p any more through a point P to a straight line l, but every line drawn through P intersects l at finite distance. From this, however, follows that there is no infinitely distant point on the line l, and any straight line thus has a finite length, runs back into itself in a finite distance. Then, also, every plane has a finite area, and the total space—that is, the universe in which such mathematics apply—has a finite volume. The space and the plane and the line are limitless, unbounded, but they are nevertheless finite in length, area or volume. The case is somewhat similar to the surface of a sphere, which is finite in area, but unlimited or boundless.

Inversely, in a centrifugal field, in which the circumference of the circle is larger than π times the diameter, the sum of the angles in a triangle is less than 180 degrees, and through a point P to a given line l two lines can be drawn, P_1 and P_2, of which the one intersects l at infinite distance to the left, the other at infinite distance to the right; and between these two "parallels" (if we define parallel as intersecting at infinity) there are an infinite number of other lines which do not intersect l and thus also can be called parallels (if we define parallel as not intersecting).

We have then three geometries: the conventional geometry of our school days, of Euclid, which applies in field-less space, and the two geometries above discussed, and then we have a more general geometry comprising all three cases, thus:

	In fieldless space	In centrifugal field	In gravitational field	Everywhere
	Euclidean, plane or parabolic. (1)	Hyperbolic geometry. (2)	Elliptic geometry. (3)	General or geometry of position. (0)
Ratio of circumference to diameter of circle........	$=\pi$	$\gtrless \pi$	$\lessgtr \pi$	No metric relations.
Triangle, sum of angles....	$= 180°$	$\lessgtr 180°$	$\gtrless 180°$	
Parallels to line through point..................	1	$2(\infty)$	0	No conception of infinity and therefore none of parallels.
Size of line, plane and space.	Infinite and unlimited.	Infinite and unlimited.	Finite in size, but unlimited, that is, without boundary.	

Our space thus varies in character between Euclidean space (1), at great distance from masses, to elliptical space (3), where it is filled by masses, and the average character of the space thus is elliptic in correspondence with the average mass density in space.

In a centrifugal field space would be hyperbolic. However, where a centrifugal field exists a gravitational field must simultaneously exist, more intense than the centrifugal force, to hold the revolving mass toward the center;[1] otherwise the mass would go out tangentially and no centrifugal force would exist. The effect of the gravitational field thus must always be greater than that of the centrifugal field, and the resultant effect is thus an elliptic form of space.

Space, that is, our universe, then must be finite, and any straight line, indefinitely extended, would finally run back into itself, close, after a length equal to several hundred million light-years. (A light-year being the distance traveled by light in one year, and light traveling 186,000 miles in one second, a light-year is about six millions of millions of miles).[2] The total volume of the universe, then, would be equal to about 4×10^{63} cubic miles.

[1] Except in a small scale, as a flywheel, where molecular forces, as the cohesion of the material, may counteract the centrifugal force and so keep the revolving mass together. However, then the field intensities are so low and the centrifugal field is so limited that its hyperbolic nature can have no effect on the universe as a whole.

[2] The "world radius" (see Lecture IV) is given by Einstein as
$$R^2 = 2/K\rho,$$
where ρ is the average density of the mass throughout the universe, and $2/K = 1.08 \times 20^{27}$ cm.

Assuming the average distance between the fixed stars as 40 light-years, their average diameter as 1,000,000 miles, and their average density equal to that of water, or 1, the average mass density of the universe would be about:
$$\rho = 3 \times 10^{-25}.$$
Thus
$$R = 10^{26} \text{ cm.}$$
$$= 60 \times 10^{20} \text{ miles}$$
$$= 100,000,000 \text{ light-years.}$$
The length of the straight line then would be:
$$l = 4R$$
$$= 400,000,000 \text{ light-years,}$$
and the volume of the universe would be
$$V = 2\pi^2 R^3$$
$$= 4 \times 10^{63} \text{ cubic miles.}$$

The expression 4×10^{63} does not look so formidable, but let us try to get a conception of it—for instance, as cents. How long would it take to count 4×10^{63} cents in money? To expedite the process we may count not in cents, nor in dollars, nor hundred-dollar bills, but in checks, as a check can be made out for a larger amount of money than any bill. We can count out about two checks per second. Let us then make these checks as large as imaginable—make each out for the total wealth of the earth—that is, the total value of all cities and villages, all fields, forests, mines and factories, all ships and railroads, in short everything existing on earth, hundreds of thousands of millions of dollars.

Suppose we count out two checks per second, each for the total wealth of the earth, and count out such checks continuously, 24 hours per day, weekdays, Sundays and holidays, and get all the thousand millions of human beings on earth to help us count out such checks, and do that from their birth to their death without ever stopping, and assume that hundreds of thousands of years ago, when man developed from his apelike ancestors, he had been put to work to count such checks, and throughout all its existence on earth the human race had spent every second to count checks, each for the total wealth of the earth, then, the total amount of money counted out, compared with 4×10^{63} cents, would not be so large as an acorn is compared with the total earth.

Thus it is impossible to get a conception of 4×10^{63}; to the human mind it is infinite.

But, while inconceivable, still it is finite, and one of the conclusions of the relativity theory is that the universe is not infinite, but is finite in volume, though unlimited.

The size of the universe is the smaller the larger the mass contained in it. It thus would follow that if the universe were entirely filled with mass, say of the density of water, it would have only a rather limited size—a few hundred million miles diameter. This puts a limit on the size of masses which can exist in the universe. Our sun, though a million times larger than the earth and nearly a million miles in diameter, is one of the smaller fixed stars. Betelgeuse (α Orionis) is estimated to have a diameter of more than 300,000,000 miles—so large that if the sun were placed in its center, Mercury, Venus and the earth, and even Mars, would still be inside of it. But if Betelgeuse had the density of water, it would about fill the whole universe; that is, the universe would have shrunk to the size of Betelgeuse. Or, in other words, the elliptic character of the universe would be so great that its total volume would only be about as large as Betelgeuse.[1] However, Betelgeuse is one of the innumerable stars in a universe so large that the enormous size of Betelgeuse from our earth appears as a mere point without any diameter. From this, then, it follows that the density of Betelgeuse must be very low, rather more like a thin gas than a solid.

I. TIME EFFECTS

In a gravitational field length is shortened, thus giving the changes of the laws of mathematics discussed above. Moreover, time is slowed down, as we have seen in discussing the effect of relative motion. That is, if we bring an accurate clock to the sun—or better still to one of the giant stars like Betelgeuse—when watching it from the earth, we would see it going slower. Now, this experiment can be made and offers the possibility of a further check on the relativity theory. We cannot carry a clock from the earth to Betelgeuse, but we do not need to do this, since every incandescent hydrogen atom, for instance, is an accurate clock, vibrating at a rate definitely fixed by the

---

[1] If the density of the body is $\rho = 1$, and this body fills the entire universe, then the world's radius would be:

$$R^2 = 1.08 \times 10^{27} \text{ cm.}$$
$$R = 36 \times 10^{12} \text{ cm.}$$
$$= 225,000,000 \text{ miles.}$$

electrical constants of the hydrogen atom and showing us
the exact rate of its vibration in the spectroscope by the
wave length or frequency of its spectrum lines.   Thus in a
strong gravitational field the frequency of luminous
vibrations of the atoms should be found slowed down; in
other words, the spectrum lines should be shifted towards
the red end of the spectrum.   The amount of this shift is so
small that it has not yet been possible to prove its existence
beyond doubt, but there seems to be some evidence of it.

LECTURE IV

THE CHARACTERISTICS OF SPACE

A. THE GEOMETRY OF THE GRAVITATIONAL FIELD

The starting point of the relativity theory is that the laws of nature, including the velocity of light in empty space, are the same everywhere and with regard to any system to which they may be referred—whether on the revolving platform of the earth or in the speeding railway train or in the space between the fixed stars. From this it follows that the length of a body is not a fixed property of it, but is relative, depending on the conditions of observation—the relative velocity of the observer with regard to the body. It also is shown that the laws of motion of bodies in a gravitational field are identical with the laws of inertial motion with regard to an accelerating system (as exemplified by the billiard ball in the speeding railway train, Lecture I). From these two conclusions it follows that in the gravitational field the circumference of a circle is not equal to π times its diameter, as we have learned to prove in our school geometry, but it is less than π times the diameter. As the theorems of mathematics depend upon each other, a change in one theorem involves a change in others. Thus from the theorem which we found to apply in a gravitational field, that "the circumference of the circle is less than π times the diameter, and this the more so the larger the diameter," it follows that the "sum of the angles in a triangle is greater than 180 degrees, and this the more so the larger the sides of the triangle." It also follows that any two lines in a plane intersect each other, that there exist no parallel lines, and that there exists no infinitely distant point on a straight line, but that all the points of a straight line are at finite distance and the total length of the straight line therefore is finite. Thus, going along a straight line in one direction, we come back to our starting point from the opposite direction, after going a finite distance—just as is the case in describing a circle. Just as the straight line is finite in length in this geometry of the gravitational field, so the plane is finite in area, though unlimited, that is, without boundary—like the surface of a sphere—and the volume of space is finite, though unlimited, and the conception of infinite distance or length or area or volume does not exist. By mathematical deduction from the relativity theory we thus derive the conclusion that our three-dimensional universe is not infinite, but finite, though inconceivably large. Although finite, it is limitless, just as the surface of a sphere is a two-dimensional space which is finite but limitless.

We have always understood that mathematics is the most exact of all sciences and its theorems capable of absolute proof, and yet here in the gravitational field we find a space in which the proven theorems of our school geometry do not hold good any more.

Mathematics is the most exact science, and its conclusions are capable of absolute proof. But this is so only because mathematics does not *attempt* to draw absolute conclusions. All mathematical conclusions are relative, conditional. It is not correct to say, "The sum of the angles in a triangle is 180 degrees," but the correct statement of the mathematical theorem is: "If certain premises or assumptions (the 'axioms') are chosen as valid, then the sum of the angles in a triangle equals 180 degrees." But whether these premises or axioms are "true"—that is, whether they are in agreement with physical experience— or not is no part of mathematics. The only requirements are that the number of axioms be sufficiently large to build conclusions or "theorems" on them and that they be consistent with each other, that is, that one does not contradict the other.

Thus we could well imagine the selection of another set of axioms, different from that of our school geometry, so as to lead to the theorem that "the sum of the angles in the triangle is less than 180 degrees," or "is more than 180 degrees," etc.

Our school geometry is built on a set of axioms which was selected by Euclid 2000 years ago, and therefore it is often called Euclidean geometry. Undoubtedly, Euclid was led by experience when selecting the axioms which he chose, and therefore the theorems of Euclidean mathematics have been in good agreement with physical experience. This, however, is no part of mathematics. It would be a problem of mathematical physics to determine which set of axioms gives closest agreement between physical space and the mathematical theorems, in other words, what are the mathematical characteristics of physical space. If, then, experience shows that under certain conditions (in a gravitational field or in a centrifugal field) the characteristics of physical space do not agree with the theorems of Euclidean mathematics, it merely means that the set of axioms on which Euclid based his geometry does not apply to this physical space, and a different set of axioms, leading to a different, non-Euclidean geometry, has to be selected. In the realm of pure mathematics there is nothing new in this. Nearly a hundred years ago the great mathematicians of the nineteenth century, the Germans Gauss and Riemann, the Russian Lobatschewsky, the Hungarian Bolyai and others, investigated the foundations of geometry, which led them to the development of systems different from the Euclidean and based on different sets of axioms. Therefore, when finally, in the relativity theory, physics advanced beyond the range of Euclidean geometry, the mathematics of the new space characteristics was already fully developed.

B. EUCLIDEAN, ELLIPTIC, HYPERBOLIC AND
PROJECTIVE GEOMETRY

Among the axioms of Euclidean geometry, such as: "Two points determine a straight line," "If two straight lines have two points in common, they have all points in common," "There are points outside of a straight line," "There are points outside of a plane," etc., there is one axiom which appears less obvious, the so-called "parallel axiom." It is:

"Through a point outside of a given straight line one, and only one, parallel line can be drawn" (the parallel line being defined as a line in the same plane which, no matter how far prolonged, never intersects the given line).

The legitimacy of this axiom has always been doubted, and throughout all the centuries since Euclid numerous attempts have been made to "prove" this parallel law; that is, to show that it is not an axiom but a theorem, a conclusion from the other axioms. All these attempts failed, and finally the great mathematicians of the nineteenth century attacked the problem from another side. Assuming that the parallel law is not an axiom, but a conclusion from other axioms, then we should be led to contradictions by choosing a different parallel law—for instance, assuming that there exist no parallels or that more than one parallel exists—and developing the conclusions from this new assumption. On the other hand, if the parallel law is a real axiom, then by assuming a different parallel law and developing the conclusions from it, we should get just as consistent a system of geometry as Euclid did, but one different from the Euclidean.

Such systems were derived from the assumption stated, thus proving that the parallel law is a real axiom and not a conclusion from other axioms. In addition to the Euclidean geometry, which is based on the axiom of one parallel, a complete geometry (called the "hyperbolic geometry") was developed on the axiom that there exist more than one parallel, and a complete geometry (the "elliptic geometry") on the axiom that no parallel exists. The latter is the geometry shown by the relativity theory to apply in a gravitational field; the former applies in a centrifugal field. Furthermore, by leaving out the parallel axiom altogether and using only the remaining axioms of Euclid, a consistent geometry was developed, the "geometry of position" (Geometrie der Lage) or "projective geometry," which is more general than the hyperbolic, elliptic and Euclidean geometries and includes these three as special cases. It deals exclusively with the relative positions of points, lines, figures, etc., but not with size and measurement. Obviously it must do thus, since it must simultaneously fit all three conditions: $C = \pi d$, $> \pi d$ and $< \pi d$.

In the following tabulation I give some of the main characteristics of the four geometries:[1]

When the mathematicians of the nineteenth century had shown that Euclid's geometry is not the only possible one, but that two other geometries existed, the elliptic and the hyperbolic, fully as consistent as Euclid's, the question arose which of the three geometries completely represents the space of physical nature.

The exact measurement of the angles in a triangle would determine this. If the physical space is non-Euclidean, the sum of the angles of the triangle would differ from 180 degrees, the more the larger the triangle. But there may be a slight departure of our space from Euclidean, which escapes notice, as the size of the triangle which we can measure is limited to a few hundred million miles.[2] The mathematicians therefore used to speculate whether such a departure would be discovered if we could measure a triangle between some distant fixed stars with some hundred light-years as sides.

The answer has now been given indirectly by the relativity theory, showing that physical space varies between

[1] Some of these properties will be explained later on.

[2] The diameter of the orbit of the earth.

	Euclidean or parabolic	Elliptic or spherical	Hyperbolic or pseudo-spherical	General geometry of position, or projective geometry [?]
Physical existence.	Fieldless space.	Gravitational field.	Centrifugal field.	General.
Characteristic of space. K.	Zero.	Positive.	Negative.	None.
Parallel axiom of plane geometry.	Through a point outside of a straight line one, and only one, parallel line can be drawn.	Any two straight lines in a plane intersect each other at finite distance; that is, parallels do not exist.	Through a point outside of a straight line two straight line can be drawn which intersect the given straight line at infinite distance, and between these two lines exist an infinite number of straight lines through the point which do not intersect the given line at all.	The conception of infinity does not exist, therefore also not the conception of parallels.
Triangles......	The sum of the angles in a triangle equals 180 degrees.	The sum of the angles in a triangle is greater than 180 degrees, the more so, the larger the sides of the triangle.	The sum of the angles in a triangle is less than 180 degrees, the more so, the larger the sides of the triangle.	Comparison of size, and measurement does not exist, and metric relations do not enter this geometry.
Circles........	The circumference of a circle equals π times the diameter.	The circumference of a circle is less than π times the diameter, the more so the larger the diameter.	The circumference of a circle is more than π times the diameter, the more so the larger the diameter.	Metric relations do not exist. The circle does not exist as a distinct figure, but merely the general conic or curve of second order.
Lines.........	The straight line is infinite in length and unlimited. It has one infinitely distant point.	The straight line is finite in length, but unlimited. It has no infinitely distant point.	The straight line is infinite in length and unlimited. It has two infinitely distant points.	
Planes........	The plane is infinite in area and unbounded.	The plane is finite in area, but unbounded.	The plane is infinite in area and unbounded.	The conception of infinity does not exist.
Space.........	Space is infinite in volume and unlimited.	Space is finite in volume, but unlimited.	Space is infinite in volume and unlimited.	
Visual conception.	Space visually appears infinite and is infinite.	Space visually appears infinite, though it is finite.	Space visually appears finite, though it is infinite.	
2-dimensional equivalent.	Plane (cylinder, cone, etc.).	Sphere (spindle, etc.).	Pseudo-sphere.	

Euclidean at great distance from masses and elliptic space at masses, and that the average space characteristic thus is not zero, but has a slight positive value, is elliptic.

It is curious that in speculating on the possible departure of space from Euclidean, in the last century, we expected to find it slightly hyperbolic. Why, I cannot remember.

C. THE EARTH AS ELLIPTIC 2-SPACE

Living in our physical space, which as far as our sense perceptions extend is Euclidean or zero-space, we cannot get outside of it to see how the world would look in an elliptic or hyperbolic space, and it therefore is difficult to get a conception of the two non-Euclidean forms of space, the positive or elliptic and the negative or hyperbolic. The only way in which we can get a partial conception is by analogy with two-dimensional spaces, or 2-spaces. We can produce the two-dimensional analogy of the two non-Euclidean spaces as surfaces, and, as three-dimensional beings, looking at these two-dimensional spaces from the outside, from a higher dimension we can see and compare their properties and characteristics with those of the Euclidean 2-space, that is, the plane.

To illustrate: Suppose our earth were surrounded by a dense mass of clouds through which sun and moon could never be seen—about as it seems to be on the planet Venus. There would then be nothing to draw our attention to the earth being a sphere floating in three-dimensional space, and our world would practically be two-dimensional, limited to the surface of the earth. The third dimension, the vertical, is accessible to us to a very limited extent only, so that we might forget it and for the moment think ourselves two-dimensional beings, limited to the surface of the earth. There would be no evidence to show us that the earth is not a flat plane. Indeed, in spite of all the evidence given by our view of the universe around it, by the sun and moon and stars and their motion, it took man many thousand years to come to the conclusion that the earth is round.

On such an earth, cut off by clouds from any view of the universe, a Euclid might develop a geometry and would produce the same axioms and theorems as we have learned in school in plane geometry. That is, the straight line would still be defined in the same way, as the shortest distance between two points, the sum of the angles in the triangle would be proven as 180 degrees, etc. Suppose now with the passing of time commerce extended on earth and ships traveled long distances. This would enable us to measure large triangles, for instance, that between New York, Rio de Janeiro and Liverpool. We would find that the sum of the angles of such a large triangle is not 180 degrees, as Euclid proved, but is materially larger. All the places lying 1000 miles from New York City we would find lying on a circle with 2000 miles diameter. But when measuring we would find the circumference of this circle materially shorter than π times 2000 miles. If we prolong a straight line on this two-dimensional surface of the earth, it does not extend into infinity, as Euclid claims, but has a finite length of 25,000 miles (the circumference of the earth), and then returns into itself. The surface of the earth is not infinite, as is that of the Euclidean plane, but is finite, though it has no limit.[1] If we prolong two parallel lines, we find that they approach nearer and nearer together and finally, after 6250 miles, intersect each other.

---

[1] When the relativity theory leads to the conclusion that the extent of our universe is not infinite, but that the volume of the universe is finite, most people will ask, "What is beyond the finite extent of the universe?" and find it difficult to conceive that there is no "beyond," but that the universe, though finite, has no limits, or, in other words, that a finite volume can be all the universe. Just as for ages it was difficult for man to conceive that the earth on which we live should not be infinite, but finite in area and still have no limit or "edge," and kept asking for an "edge" of the world. We got over this by familiarity and have no difficulty to conceive a surface like that of the earth, which is finite in area but without boundary. Analogous thereto is the universe of the relativity theory—finite in volume, but without limit or boundary.

In short, we find that the geometry on the surface of the earth is not the Euclidean geometry, but is the elliptic geometry of the mathematicians of the nineteenth century, the same which the relativity theory shows to apply in the gravitational field. When measuring the surface of the earth, we therefore cannot use the Euclidean geometry and the trigonometry corresponding thereto, the plane trigonometry of our school days, except on a small scale, as when surveying the lots of a city. When surveying countries and continents, we have to use the trigonometric formulas of the elliptic geometry, in which the sum of the angles of the triangle is greater than 180 degrees.

Thus the non-Euclidean geometry which the relativity theory introduced into physics, after all, is nothing so very new. A part of the plane or two-dimensional elliptic geometry, its trigonometry, is in every day use in surveying the earth and is quite familiar. We all had it in school under the name of "spherical trigonometry." Spherical trigonometry thus is the trigonometry of the elliptic plane geometry. However, when studying spherical trigonometry, we usually take advantage of our being three-dimensional beings, and so do not limit ourselves to the surface of the sphere, but project outside of it into the third dimension. Naturally, in three-dimensional geometry we could not do this, as we have no fourth dimension beyond it. But, rigidly, we could develop the spherical trigonometry, and the geometry of the spherical surface, perfectly well without ever going outside of the surface into a higher or third dimension. So we have to do in three-dimensional geometry, where we have no higher dimension to go to. After all, we apply the same looseness of usage in plane geometry, for instance, when proving two figures as congruent by bringing them to coincidence. Sometimes we can do this by moving the one figure in the plane into coincidence with the other, but sometimes we cannot do this without turning the one figure over in the third dimension—when two figures are symmetrical like the impressions of the right and the left hand. But, strictly, this is not permissible in plane geometry, and we should distinguish between congruent alike and symmetrical. In solid geometry we have to do so. A right-handed and a left-handed screw may be identical in every part, but still are not alike, as they cannot be brought into coincidence, because we cannot turn one over through a fourth dimension.[1]

The plane or two-dimensional elliptic geometry, therefore, is the geometry in the surface of a sphere, while the plane or two-dimensional Euclidean geometry is the geometry in a plane, and the plane or two-dimensional hyperbolic geometry is the geometry in a so-called pseudo-spherical surface. (Fig. 24.)

This is rather disappointing. We were led to a new non-Euclidean geometry, in which the straight line has only a finite length, the plane a finite area, the angles of the triangles are more than 180 degrees, and other strange features exist, and then find that this is merely the geometry of the surface of a sphere, and the straight line of finite length is merely a largest circle, etc.

We spoke of a straight line on the earth, and large triangles, like that between New York, Liverpool and Rio de Janeiro, in which the sum of the angles is greater than 180 degrees. But you will say that the path in which a ship travels from New York to Liverpool is not a straight line, but is a circle, a "largest circle" of the earth, and the straight line between New York and Liverpool passes through the interior of the earth. The straight line between New York and Liverpool, which goes through the interior of the earth, is not a part of the earth's surface, but belongs to a higher dimensional space. What, then, is the straight line of the earth's surface? A straight line has been defined physically as the shortest distance between two points. In the two-

---

[1] Thus, if a magician or spiritist claims the existence of a fourth dimension, ask him to prove it by taking a right-handed glove from some one in the audience and returning it as a left-handed glove. He would have to turn it over in the fourth dimension.

dimensional geometry of the earth's surface the shortest
distance between two points is the largest circle, and this
therefore is the straight line of the spherical surface. Or,
a straight line has been defined as the path of a body moving without any force acting on it. Such a body in a
spherical surface moves in the largest circle. The mathematical definition of the straight line is "the line determined by two points." This probably is the best definition.
Analytically it means that the straight line is the line
defined by an equation of the first degree. In the two-
dimensional elliptic space which we call a spherical surface
the largest circle therefore is the straight line and as seen
fulfills all the characteristics of the straight line, and
within the spherical surface the largest circle has no curvature; that is, it is the same as our straight line in three-
dimensional space is to us. Nevertheless, looking at the
"straight line" of the spherical surface from the outside,
from higher space, we see it curved, and therefore the
mathematicians often use the term "the straightest line."
But in this respect it is in no way different from the straight
line of our three-dimensional space which we get, as the
shortest distance, by stretching a string between two points.
We do not know whether what we call a straight line in
our three-dimensional space would still be a straight line
in a four-dimensional space of which our three-dimensional
space was a part (and mathematically we can conceive
such a space). Or, rather, when we speak of a straight
line in our three-dimensional space, because it is determined
by two points and is the shortest distance between these
two points, we know that this line, from a four-dimensional
Euclidean space of which our space is a part, is not always
straight, is not always the shortest distance between two
points, but may be curved, just as the straight line of the
spherical 2-space is curved seen from 3-space. For
instance, when the earth and the planet Mars are nearly at
opposite sides of the sun, the straight line between the
earth and Mars, which passes close to the sun, is straight

only in our space, but as a line in a Euclidean 4-space, which contains our 3-space, it is curved[1] and another line is a shorter distance between earth and Mars, but this other line passes out of our 3-space into 4-space and therefore does not exist for us. As seen then, the "straight line" has a meaning only with reference to the space in which it is defined, but a straight line of one space may not be a straight line for a higher space.

Furthermore, while from and as a part of Euclidean 3-space, the elliptic 2-space appears curved, as a sphere, if we could look at it as a part of an elliptic 3-space of the same characteristic constant as the elliptic 2-space, the latter would not appear curved, as sphere, but flat, and the straight line of this elliptic 2-space would not appear curved, as circle, but straight. But an Euclidean plane and a straight line in it, as a part of elliptic 3-space, would appear curved (or as much of the plane or line as can be obtained in elliptic 3-space). Broadly then, any space, straight line or plane seen from and as part of a higher space of different characteristic appears curved, and it appears plane or straight only as part of a higher space of the same characteristic constant, as will be seen later.

D. THE CHARACTERISTIC OR CURVATURE OF SPACE

There is only one physical space for us, the space in which we are living, which is practically a Euclidean 3-space. We cannot go beyond this space, and therefore find it difficult to get a conception of the two non-Euclidean spaces, the elliptic and the hyperbolic, as we cannot look at them from the outside and see their characteristics and properties. The only way to get a partial conception of these non-Euclidean spaces is by analogy with the corresponding two-dimensional spaces, that is, surfaces. Just as the plane is the 2-space corresponding to our physical

[1] Because it passes through the gravitational field of the sun, that is, a region of elliptic 3-space.

3-space, and as in school we first studied the geometry of the 2-space, or plane geometry, and then advanced to the geometry of the 3-space, or solid geometry, so we can construct and produce the elliptic and the hyperbolic 2-space, which correspond to the elliptic and hyperbolic 3-space in the same way as the Euclidean plane corresponds to the Euclidean or physical 3-space.

These Euclidean, elliptic and hyperbolic 2-spaces we can, as three-dimensional beings, see from the outside and so get a complete conception of their characteristics and of the elliptic and hyperbolic plane geometry which corresponds to the Euclidean plane geometry.

It is characteristic of the three types of 2-space or surface that the circumference of the circle is equal, larger or smaller than π times the diameter. That is, the quantity $C/2\pi r$ (where C is the circumference of a circle with radius r) equals one in Euclidean space, is less than one in elliptic and more than one in hyperbolic space. Thus the quantity

$$1 - C/2\pi r \qquad (1)$$

equals zero in Euclidean space, is positive in elliptic and negative in hyperbolic space, and therefore to a certain extent characterizes the space. However, as the circumference of the circle differs from $2\pi r$ the more the larger the diameter, the quantity (1) is not constant, but depends on the radius r. It can be shown, however, that the quantity[1]

$$K = \frac{6}{r^2}\left(1 - \frac{C}{2\pi r}\right) \qquad (2)$$

is independent of the numerical value of the radius r and is constant for each kind of space. It therefore is called the *characteristic constant of the space*, or sometimes, for reasons which we will see later, the *curvature* of the space.

In Euclidean space the characteristic constant K is zero, and the Euclidean space therefore also is called zero space, or plane space, or parabolic space.

---

[1] In this expression higher terms have been neglected, and it therefore is an approximation only, which holds when $(1 - C/2\pi r)$ is a small quantity.

In elliptic space the characteristic constant K is positive, and the larger the more the elliptic space differs from Euclidean. Elliptic space therefore may also be called positive space; that is, space with positive constant.

In hyperbolic space the characteristic constant K is negative, and the larger the more the hyperbolic space differs from Euclidean. Hyperbolic space, therefore, may also be called negative space; that is, space with negative constant.

Let a straight line be drawn through two points of the curve shown in Fig. 18 and these two points be brought

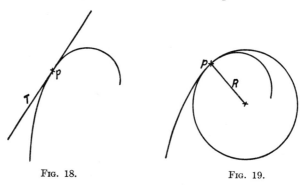

Fig. 18.   Fig. 19.

infinitely near together. The line then becomes the tangent T of the curve and represents the *direction* of the curve at the point p where it touches.

Let now a circle be drawn through three points of the curve and these three points be brought infinitely near together. The circle then osculates the curve, as seen in Fig. 19—that is, touches it at three successive points—and therefore has at these points the same curvature as the curve. That is, it represents the curvature of the curve at its contact point p, and the radius R of this circle is the *radius of curvature* of the curve, and its reciprocal.

$$K_1 = 1/R, \tag{3}$$

is called the *curvature* of the curve. (The *reciprocal* of the radius is called the curvature, as a curve is called the more curved the smaller its radius. Radius $R = \infty$ gives zero curvature or the straight line.)

When we come to surfaces, that is, two-dimensional spaces, we find that we have at every point of the surface an infinite number of tangents, in different directions, which all lie in a tangent plane. We also find that in every point we have an infinite number of osculating circles and therefore radii of curvatures, which all lie in the normal to the surface at the point. Among this infinite number of radii are two radii at right angles to each other, R_1 and R_2, which are extremes, either one the shortest and the other the longest or both the shortest, but in opposite directions. The curvature of the surface at the point is measured by the product of the two main radii of curvature, and as the *curvature* of the surface is denoted the value:

$$K_2 = 1/R_1R_2. \tag{4}$$

It can be shown that the characteristic constant (2) of the 2-space, K, is equal to K_2 (4); that is, is the curvature of the 2-space. That is:

$$K = \frac{6}{r^2}\left(1 - \frac{C}{2\pi r}\right) = \frac{1}{R_1R_2} = \frac{1}{R^2} \tag{5}$$

is the *characteristic constant* of the 2-space or the *curvature* of the surface which represents this 2-space.

Instead of speaking of the characteristic constant of the space, we therefore often speak of the "*curvature of space.*"

The Euclidean space thus is a space of zero curvature.

The elliptic space is a space of positive curvature.

The hyperbolic space is a space of negative curvature.

Characteristic of all three spaces is constancy of curvature.

$$R = \sqrt{R_1R_2} = \frac{1}{\sqrt{K}} \tag{6}$$

then may be called the *radius* of the space.

In elliptic space,

$$l = 2\pi R \tag{7}$$

is the length of the straight line.

$$A = 4\pi R^2 \tag{8}$$

is the area or surface of the plane.

$$V = 4\pi^2 R^3/3 \tag{9}$$

is the volume of the 3-space.

In Euclidean space, $K = 0$, thus $R = \infty$; that is, the radius of the Euclidean space is infinity.

In the hyperbolic space K is negative, and R thus becomes imaginary; that is, the radius of the hyperbolic space is imaginary.

Elliptic 2-space, therefore, is a surface having constant curvature of radius R; that is, it is a sphere, and the elliptic geometry is the geometry on a sphere of radius

$$R = 1/\sqrt{K}. \tag{10}$$

In Euclidean 3-space the equation of a 2-space of constant curvature K is given by

$$K\left\{ x^2 + y^2 + \left(z - \frac{1}{\sqrt{K}}\right)^2 \right\} = 1. \tag{11}$$

For $K = 0$ this gives:

$$z = 0; \tag{12}$$

that is, the xy plane, or a Euclidean 2-space.

For K differing from zero, shifting the coördinate center by $1/\sqrt{K}$ gives:

$$K(x^2 + y^2 + z^2) = 1. \tag{13}$$

For positive value of K this is a sphere of radius:

$$R = 1/\sqrt{K}. \tag{14}$$

For negative value of K,

$$K = -1/R^2,$$

it is:

$$x^2 + y^2 + z^2 = -R^2;$$

that is, all points x, y, z are imaginary.

Thus in Euclidean 3-space no real (complete) hyperbolic

2-space exists, but the hyperbolic 2-space appears as a sphere with imaginary radius:

$$R = j/\sqrt{K}. \tag{15}$$

E. THE STRAIGHT LINE AND THE ELLIPTIC 2-SPACE

In a surface or 2-space, as a plane, a line may be bent to the right, as a in Fig. 20, or to the left, as z. We can imagine the line gradually changed from a to b, c, etc., to z. In a it is bent to the right, in z to the left, and when changing from a to z it therefore must sometime pass through a position s, where it is not bent to the right any more, nor yet bent to the left—that is, where it is straight; in other words, where it has no bend in the 2-space or as line or element of the 2-space and hence is a straight line of the 2-space, whatever the 2-space may be, whether a zero-space, that is, a Euclidean plane, or an elliptic 2-space,

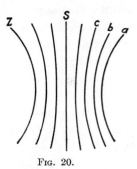

Fig. 20.

which seen from our Euclidean 3-space appears as a sphere etc. This straight line may be bent into a direction at right angles to the 2-space, out of the 2-space into a third dimension, for instance into the Euclidean 3-space (our physical space), from which we see the 2-space, and then would appear as a circle. Or it may appear straight even from the 3-space, this depending on whether the characteristic of the 3-space is the same or different from that of the 2-space.

I may have a straight line L in an elliptic 2-space S, which is contained in our Euclidean 3-space (that is, a largest circle L on sphere S in Euclidean 3-space). I can put a Euclidean 2-space—that is, a Euclidean plane P—through the line L. For the elliptic 2-space S, L is a straight line. For the Euclidean 2-space P, L is a circle. I may put another elliptic 2-space S', of lesser characteristic constant—that is, a sphere of larger radius—through *L*. On *S'*, *L* will be curved, but less than on *P*. (But I could not put an elliptic 2-space of greater curvature through *L*; that is, seen from Euclidean 3-space, put through a circle a sphere of smaller radius than that of the circle, so that the circle lies on the sphere.)

The elliptic 2-space *S*, as part of the Euclidean 3-space, appears curved, as sphere. But I could, at least mathematically, consider *S* as an elliptic 2-space contained in an elliptic 3-space of the same constant, and seen from this elliptic 3-space, *S* would not be curved, but would appear plane, as a flat plane, of finite area. The elliptic 2-space *S* would then be in common to the Euclidean 3-space and the elliptic 3-space, and in the Euclidean 3-space *S* would be a sphere, but in the elliptic 3-space *S* would be a flat plane of finite area. Any straight line on *S* would also be a straight line for the elliptic 3-space, but would be a circle for the Euclidean 3-space, a "largest circle" of the sphere *S*. I may consider *S* as contained in an elliptic 3-space of lesser curvature than that of *S*. In this 3-space *S* would still appear curved, but less so than it appears in the Euclidean 3-space; that is, it would appear as a sphere of larger radius. But we could not consider the elliptic 2-space *S* as a part of an elliptic 3-space of greater curvature than *S*. If we could consider the elliptic 2-space *S* as a part of an elliptic 3-space of greater curvature than that of *S*, *S* would again appear curved, but not as sphere, but now with hyperbolic or negative curvature, and that would make it an imaginary sphere, as we have seen above. *S* could not as a whole be contained in the elliptic 3-space of greater curvature. The reason is that the straight lines in the 3-space are finite in length and shorter than the straight lines on the 2-space *S*, when the latter has a lesser curvature, and the latter therefore cannot be contained in the 3-space. Thus only a distorted part of *S* could find room in the 3-space, as pseudo-sphere.

In other words, a 2-space can be contained in a 3-space of lesser curvature, but not in a 3-space of greater curvature. Thus a hyperbolic 3-space can contain elliptic 2-spaces and Euclidean 2-spaces and hyperbolic 2-spaces of lesser negative curvature; a Euclidean 3-space can contain only Euclidean and elliptic 2-spaces, but no complete hyperbolic 2-space, and an elliptic 3-space can contain only elliptic 2-spaces of the same or greater curvature, the former appearing as planes, the latter as spheres.

It thus follows that, absolutely, there exists no such thing as a "straight line," but "straight line" is relative only, with reference to the space in which it is defined. Any straight line with regard to a space of higher dimension than the space in which it is a straight line may not be a straight line; it is a straight line if the higher space has the same curvature, but is curved in a higher space of different curvature.

This is exactly the case in our physical space, which as the relativity theory shows, has a slight positive curvature. If we could imagine our three-dimensional space as contained in and as a part of a four-dimensional Euclidean space (and mathematically there is no difficulty in this), then from this four-dimensional Euclidean space we would see that the straight lines of our space are really circles with about 100,000,000 light-years' radius. But the center of the circle and its curvature are outside of our 3-space, in the fourth dimension, exactly as the straight line of the elliptic 2-space is a circle seen from the Euclidean 3-space containing the elliptic 2-space as sphere, but a circle of which the center and the curvature are outside of the 2-space, and within the 2-space it has no curvature.

Thus, also, what we see as a plane in our space, from the four-dimensional Euclidean space in which our space is contained, would be seen as a sphere with 100,000,000 light-years' radius, and our entire three-dimensional space would be a three-dimensional hypersurface, finite but unlimited, in the Euclidean 4-space. But while we mathematically

can conceive of such a "hypersurface," physically we
cannot.

F. BENDING OF SPACE

Suppose in a Euclidean 2-space—that is, a plane like the
sheet of paper on which is printed Fig. 21—we have two
points, P_1 and P_2. Through these two points we can put
one, and only one, straight line, L_0. This is the shortest
distance between the two points P_1 and P_2, and any other
line between them, as L_1 or L_2—shown dotted in Fig. 21—

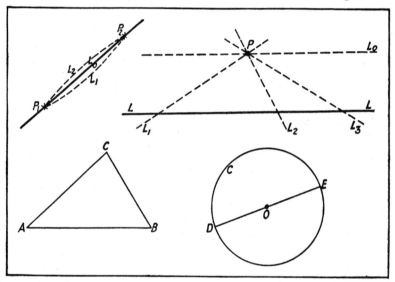

Fig. 21.

is longer. Suppose we have a straight line L in the plane
Fig. 21 and a point P outside of L. Any line drawn in the
plane through point P, as L_1, L_2, L_3, etc. (shown dotted),
intersects the line L, except one line L_0, which no matter
how far it is produced does not intersect L and is called the
parallel. From this it follows that in a triangle ABC the
sum of the angles equals 180 degrees, and that in any circle
the circumference C is π times the diameter DOE of the
circle.

Suppose now we take the plane of Fig. 21—the sheet of paper—and bend it in any desired manner, but without stretching it. We may bend it into a cylinder or a cornucopia—that is, a cone—or into a corrugated sheet as shown in Fig. 22.[1] Looking at it now, from outside space, the lines L, L_0, L_1, the sides of the triangle ABC, etc., are not straight any more, but curved. But within the plane of the paper the dimensions all remain the same, and if we measure the sides of the triangle or the circumference of the circle, the angles, areas, etc., with a rule or measure contained within the plane of the paper (that is, within the 2-space, the rule therefore in the 3-space bending with the paper), we then find exactly the same measurements as before we bent the plane into a cylinder or corrugated shape. The line L_0, though not appearing straight any more from the outside, still is, within the sheet of paper, shorter than the lines L_1 and L_2 and still is the shortest path between the points P_1 and P_2—that is, still is the "straight line" of the 2-space—and L_0 still never intersects L—that is, remains the parallel. Thus all the geometry which we derived and proved in the Euclidean plane (Fig. 21) still holds just the same in a cylinder, a cone, a corrugated sheet or any other 2-space which we may produce by bending this Euclidean plane, and there is no way and no possibility to show and prove from the inside of the 2-space (Figs. 21 and 22) whether we have bent it out of shape or not. Indeed, there is no such thing as bending the 2-space *per se* out of shape, but we have bent it only with regard to its location with respect to the 3-space from which we look at it.

The same thing applies to an elliptic or hyperbolic 2-space. We may take a piece of a sphere (Fig. 23 or 27) and bend it—always without stretching—into a spindle, as in

---

[1] This figure and figures 23, 24, 26, 27, 28 and 34 are printed stereoscopically on pages 125 through 137, so that the reader may cut them out and look at them through a stereoscope to see the curvature. With a little practice it is possible to see stereoscopically without a stereoscope (see note on page 123).

Fig. 28. All dimensions measured within the surface have remained the same, and a two-dimensional being living within the surface could never find out whether he was in the surface of a sphere, or of a spindle, or of some other shape produced by bending. The straight lines of the sphere—that is, seen from the outside, its largest circles— also are the straight lines of the spindle—that is, the shortest lines between two points; the angles are the same, etc. Thus the characteristic constant, or the curvature of the space, remains unchanged by the bending of the space.

Euclidean 2-space thus is the plane and any surface made by bending it or a part of it in any desired manner— into cylinder, cone, wave surface, etc; elliptic 2-space is the sphere and any surface made by bending a piece of the sphere into some other shape, as a spindle; hyperbolic 2-space is the pseudo-sphere—not existing in Euclidean 3-space—or any surface which can be considered as made by bending a piece of the pseudo-sphere into some other shape as shown in Fig. 24.

But it must be bending without stretching. If, for instance, in bending the plane Fig. 21 I stretch it at some places, contract it at others, the line L_0 between P_1P_2 of Fig. 21 may be stretched and so may become longer than lines L_1 or L_2, and therefore will cease to be the shortest line—that is, the straight line of the bent space—and the geometry of this space would not remain the same.

This illustrates the relativity of the conception "straight line." The shortest path between two points P_1 and P_2 of the cylinder or cone looks very different to us from a straight line, and still it is geometrically identical with the straight line of our plane geometry; and it becomes like it in looks on simply unrolling the cone or cylinder—an operation which makes no change whatever within the surface, but merely changes its relation to a higher dimensional space.

However, when we bend a 2-space into some other shape we may get "kinks" or "singular points" into it, and at these singular points conditions may become indefinite; and in the geometry on a surface with such singular points we have to take care to arrange our figures so that they keep away from the singular points. For instance, we can bend a plane into a cone, and the geometry on the cone therefore is identical with the plane geometry of our school days, but when drawing figures on the cone—straight lines like the lines traced by a string stretched on the cone—we must keep away from the point of the cone. So the geometry on the spindle is the geometry on the sphere, but while on the sphere we may draw the figures anywhere, on the spindle we have to keep the lines of the figure away from the two points of the spindle, as singular points.

This possibility of bending a space into some other form without change of its constant permits us to illustrate hyperbolic geometry on a real surface. As has been seen, a complete hyperbolic 2-space cannot exist in Euclidean 3-space. But in Fig. 24 is shown a picture of a hyperbolic 2-space which bears to the complete hyperbolic 2-space about the same relation as the cone in Euclidean 2-space bears to the plane. It is Beltrami's pseudo-sphere, the rotation surface of the tractrix[1] as meridian curve.

As seen, Beltrami's pseudo-sphere has a singular point at infinity—that is, the surface points into infinity in two opposite directions (the lower side is cut shorter in the model)—and a singular line, a circular knife edge. Taking the precaution to draw the figures on the pseudo-sphere so that they do not run into the singular line and the singular point, we can study the hyperbolic geometry on it.

[1] The tractrix is the curve described by a weight at one end of a rod when the other end of the rod is dragged along a straight line. That is, it is the curve given by the condition, that the length of the tangent of the curve is constant. Its equation is:

$$y = k \, \log \frac{k + \sqrt{k^2 - x^2}}{x} - \sqrt{k^2 - x^2}$$

G. MATHEMATICAL SPACE AND PHYSICAL SPACE

We must sharply distinguish between physical space and mathematical space. Mathematical space is the conception of a dimensional continuous manifold, and an infinite number of different mathematical spaces, of any number of dimensions, can be conceived and have the same reality in the science of mathematics as philosophical conceptions. Physical space is the form of conception in which our mind clothes the (supposed) extraneous cause of our sense perceptions. There is therefore only one physical space, and it exists only as a form of something acting on our senses; that is, exists only as far as there is something filling space, and "empty space" in this respect has no meaning. As physical space is a dimensional continuous manifold, it is of interest thus to ask which of the innumerable conceivable mathematical spaces agrees best with the properties of physical space. Mathematical space itself has nothing to do with nature and things in nature, but is entirely conceptional.

The only characteristic required and assumed for the "point" as the element of mathematical space is the property of continuity. That is, to any point you can get other points infinitely close and can thus go continuously from one point to another. Such is for instance, the case with the instances of time, with the temperatures, colors, etc.

The "straight line" then is defined by the axiom:

"Two points a and b determine one and only one straight line L."

The straight line contains an infinite number of points, which are given by:

$$p_1 = \frac{xa + yb}{x + y}. \tag{1}$$

Each point p_1 is determined by a ratio $x \div y$, and this ratio is called its coördinate.

We extend beyond the straight line by the axiom:
"There are points outside of the straight line."

Any such point c with any point p_1 of the line L gives again a line, and any point on this line is given by:

$$p_2 = \frac{x'c + y'p_1}{x' + y'} = \frac{xa + yb + zc}{x + y + z}. \tag{2}$$

The ratios $x \div y \div z$, then, are called the coördinates of the point p_2. The infinite number of points p_1 of the first straight line L give an infinite number of straight lines, and as each of these straight lines has an infinite number of points p_2, the number of points p_2 thus is infinitely larger than that of the points p_1. The totality of the points p_2, therefore, is called a two-dimensional manifold, or a mathematical 2-space, or a mathematical plane.

We extend beyond the plane by the axiom:
"There are points outside of the plane."

Any such point d with any of the ∞^2 points p_2 gives ∞^2 lines, and each of these lines contains an infinite number of points p_3, given by:

$$p_3 = \frac{x''d + y''p_2}{x'' + y''} = \frac{xa + yb + zc + ud}{x + y + z + u} \tag{3}$$

so that infinite times as many points p_3 exist as points p_2, and the points p_3 thus constitute a three-dimensional manifold or mathematical 3-space. Each of these points p_3 is given by its coördinates, the three ratios: $x \div y \div z \div u$.

Mathematically, we extend in the same manner beyond the 3-space by the axiom:
"There are points outside of the 3-space."[1]

Any such point e again gives a straight line with any of the ∞^3 points, and so leads to ∞^4 points,

$$p_4 = \frac{xa + yb + cz + ud + ve}{x + y + z + u + v}, \tag{4}$$

given by the coördinates $x \div y \div z \div u \div v$ and constituting a four-dimensional manifold or mathematical 4-space.

---

[1] This axiom disagrees with physical experience, therefore all the mathematical spaces from here on have no physical representation.

In this manner we can build up to any number of dimensions, and as a mathematical conception the n-dimensional manifold, or n-space, is just as real as the 3-space or 2-space. The mathematical n-space merely is the continuous mani-

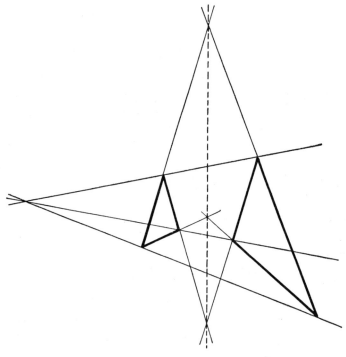

Fig. 25.

fold of ∞^n elements which are given by the n ratios: $x : y : z : u \ . \ . \ . \ x_n$ as coördinates.

As the physical space is a three-dimensional manifold of physical points—that is, positions in space—it could be represented by some mathematical 3-space, while the surface of a physical body could be represented by some mathematical 2-space, etc.

As in these mathematical spaces we have defined points, lines and planes, etc., we can deal with triangles, polygons, space figures, etc., and so can construct a geometry of mathematical 2-space, or plane geometry, a geometry of mathematical 3-space, or solid geometry, of mathematical *n*-space, etc. These geometries, however, would be entirely geometries of position, or projective geometries (the case 4 of page 74); that is, they would deal only with the location of points and lines, etc., to each other, but not with the sizes and metric relations, with equality, etc. Thus, they contain theorems like Fig. 25.

"If the three lines connecting corresponding corners of two triangles meet in one point, the three points of intersection of corresponding sides lie in a straight line."

But we could not have a theorem reading:

"Two triangles are congruent if their corresponding sides are equal,"
or:

"The sum of the squares of the two sides of a right-angled triangle equals the square of the hypotenuse."

All metric relations, comparison of sizes, measurements, etc., are based on bringing figures into coincidence, for instance, the measuring rod with the measured length, etc. We prove the congruence of two triangles by moving one into coincidence with the other. Before this is possible in the mathematical spaces defined above we must add an axiom specifying that:

"A figure can be moved in space without changing."

This is by no means obvious. It is the case, for instance, in the surface of a sphere, but it is not the case in the surface of an egg-shaped figure. We can thus have a theorem of two congruent triangles in the sphere and prove it by moving the one triangle into coincidence with the other. But we could not have two congruent triangles in the surface of an egg, because we could not move one triangle from a part of the egg's surface to another one, where the curvature is different, without distorting it, stretching some dimensions and contracting others, and thereby changing the dimensions. Thus measurements on the surface of the egg and theorems on metric relations, as the Phythagorean theorem, are impossible.

It is not possible to move figures from one space to another space of different curvature, for instance, from a sphere into a plane, without stretching and thereby changing and thereby distorting the dimensional relations. Thus figures in one space cannot be represented in correct dimension in another space. (Hence the difficulty in map making: to represent a part of the earth's surface, of a sphere, on a plane map with the least possible distortion of dimensions.)

This axiom of metric relations expressed mathematically means that the characteristic or curvature of space K is constant.

Thus, not all spaces are metric spaces—that is, spaces in which measurements are possible and in which we can speak of and compare the sizes of figures, deal with equality, congruence, infinity, etc. The general space is projective—that is, merely positional relations exist in it— and a special condition or axiom is required, that of constancy of curvature, to establish metric relations.

Positionally, there is no difference between finite and infinitely distant elements of space, and the geometry of position, or projective geometry, thus does not contain the conception of the infinitely distant. The distinctions based on the relation to the infinitely distant—for instance, the differences between the ellipsis, which is all finite, and the hyperbola, which runs into infinity—are thus absent in it. This does not mean that infinitely distant elements may not exist in the geometry of position and that all the elements of projective geometry are finite (as all the elements of the elliptic geometry are finite). But it means that in their projective properties infinitely distant elements differ in no way from finite elements. All the difference between finite and infinitely distant elements is metric, and the conception of infinitely distant elements as different from finite elements is introduced only by the metric axioms.

While mathematical spaces may be conceived as of any number of dimensions and have equal reality as mathematical conceptions, physical space is limited by experience to three dimensions—that is, any point in physical space is determined by three data or coördinates, for instance, the three distances x, y, z from some arbitrarily chosen coördinate axes.

It must be realized, however, that the three-dimensional character of physical space is in reality not entirely empirical, but also is conceptional. Physical space is three-dimensional when considering the point as the element of physical space; that is, any point in physical space is determined by three coördinates, x, y, z. But in the real physical space of our experience there are no points, but bodies, and the point is a mere mathematical conception, an abstraction, but not a physically existing thing. Thus the three-dimensional physical point-space also is a mere abstraction and is no more a physical reality than its element, the mathematical point, is. What is real is the physical body. But the location of a (rigid) body in physical space is not fixed by three coördinates, but requires six coördinates. Three coördinates, x_1, y_1, z_1, would fix one point, P_1, of the body, for instance, its center of mass. This would not fix the body, for the body could still have an infinite number of positions in turning around its center point, P_1. We must thus fix a second point, P_2. With point P_1 fixed, P_2 can move anywhere on the surface of a sphere with P_1 as center and P_1P_2 as radius. As the surface of the sphere is two-dimensional, two data or coördinates, x_2, y_2, thus are necessary to fix point P_2 on this sphere. Fixing the two points P_1 and P_2, however, does not yet locate the body; it still can turn around the axis P_1P_2. A third point, P_3, thus has still to be fixed. As P_3 could move on a circle around P_1P_2 as axis, one coördinate, x_3, is sufficient to fix point P_3 and thereby locate the body in space.

Thus six data or coördinates, x_1, y_1, z_1, x_2, y_2, x_3, are required to locate the position of the rigid body in physical space, and as empirically the body is the element of physical space, we might speak of the physical space of our experience as six-dimensional and not three-dimensional.

This is not a mere quibbling, but is very real, and all through physics and mechanics we find that not three but six data or coördinates are required to locate an element in physical space, whether a position, a motion or the cause of a motion, that is, a force. Thus:

The location of a body in space is given by six coördinates, as above shown, or by nine coördinates, those of three points of the body, with three equations between them (which represent the constancy of the distances between the points):

$$x_1, y_1, z_1, \quad s_{12}{}^2 = (x_1 - x_2)^2 + (y_1 - y_2)^2 + (z_1 - z_2)^2.$$
$$x_2, y_2, z_2, \quad s_{13}{}^2 = (x_1 - x_3)^2 + (y_1 - y_3)^2 + (z_1 - z_3)^2.$$
$$x_3, y_3, z_3, \quad s_{23}{}^2 = (x_2 - x_3)^2 + (y_2 - y_3)^2 + (z_2 - z_3)^2.$$

The motion of a body from one position in physical space to another position is given by six independent components, of which for convenience three are usually chosen as translations, in the direction of the coördinate axes:

$$v_1, v_2, v_3,$$

and the other three as rotations around the coördinate axes:

$$r_1, r_2, r_3.$$

The total force acting upon a body is expressed by six independent components, of which usually three are chosen as vector forces along the coördinate axes:

$$F_1, F_2, F_3,$$

and the other three as couples or torques around the axes:

$$T_1, T_2, T_3.$$

As in physical and mechanical calculations we almost always have to come to the abstraction of the "point" as an element of our calculation, it is more convenient to consider the mathematical point as space element and treat the six coördinates of the physical body not as dimensions but as "degrees of freedom." We must realize, however, that the statement of the three dimensions of physical space is not direct experience but already includes a mathematical abstraction.

Thus by choosing something else than the mathematical point as space element we can consider physical space as of a different number of dimensions.

For instance, any point in physical space can be considered as center of an infinite number of spheres, of different radii r. As there are ∞^3 points in space, given by their coördinates x, y, z, and each as center gives rise to ∞ spheres, given by their radii r, there are therefore existing in our physical space ∞^4 spheres, represented by their coördinates x, y, z, r. That is, with the sphere as element, physical space is four-dimensional, and a four-dimensional geometry —at least a projective or non-metric geometry—can be constructed in physical space with the sphere as element or "point." This has been done.[1]

Following our outline as above:

Let s_1, s_2, s_3, s_4, s_5 be five spheres in space. Then any of the ∞^4 spheres is given by:

$$s = x_1 s_1 + x_2 s_2 + x_3 s_3 + x_4 s_4 + x_5 s_5,$$

with four coördinates, the four ratios:

$$x_1 \div x_2 \div x_3 \div x_4 \div x_5$$

Three linear equations between the x then give a "line," just as two equations in the three Cartesian coördinates give a line in three-dimensional point space. This "line" in 4-space consists of all the spheres which intersect in a circle, etc.

As has been seen, therefore, in spite of all our conviction of the three-dimensionality of space, in reality space and the number of dimensions of space are relative, dependent on the condition of the observer—that is, on the thing chosen as element of the space—and physical space with the point as element may be three-dimensional. With the sphere as element it is four-dimensional, with the rigid

[1] Reye, "Geometrie der Kugeln."

body as element six-dimensional. Thus space and time and dimension are relative.[1]

H. THE BUNDLE AS ELLIPTIC 2-SPACE

We try to get a conception of non-Euclidean space, as the elliptic space of the gravitational field and the hyperbolic space of the centrifugal field, by considering the corresponding two-dimensional spaces. These we can construct as surfaces in our physical 3-space, and so can study them, by looking at them from a higher dimension as part of our 3-space. The disadvantage, however, is that we can look at these various 2-spaces from one 3-space only, our physical space, which is essentially Euclidean, and then it is difficult to abstract and realize which of the properties and characteristics of the 2-space are inherent in the 2-space and which are merely incidental to the relation of the 2-space with our particular 3-space and would not be the same when seen from some other 3-space, and therefore are not essentially characteristic of the 2-space. Thus we have seen that the elliptic 2-space, or "elliptic plane," appears from our Euclidean 3-space as a spherical surface, and the straight line of the elliptic 2-space appears as a circle in the Euclidean 3-space; that is, as curved. We realize that this line has no curvature, is straight, in the elliptic 2-space. But still, it is curved into the Euclidean 3-space, and as we look at it from the Euclidean 3-space, it is difficult to avoid the feeling that, after all, it is not a straight line but a curve, and only appears straight in the elliptic 2-space because from this space we cannot see the curvature. The same applies to

[1] The fallacy of the magician's or spiritist's four-dimensional space is not in the conception of a four-dimensional space in general, but in the conception of a four-dimensional *point* space—in claiming a dimension higher than shown by experience. Physical space is a three-dimensional point space, and attributing to it a higher dimension with the point as space element, therefore, is against experience. But not so with something else as element. On the contrary, with something else chosen as element of physical space, we may expect to find it with a different number of dimensions.

the elliptic 2-space as a whole; from within we can notice no curvature, and it is an elliptic plane, but from Euclidean 3-space we plainly see it curved, as sphere, and so cannot entirely avoid the feeling that after all it is not plane but is curved, and that it appears plane from within merely because from within we cannot see the curvature. We may explain that from an elliptic 3-space of the same curvature the elliptic 2-space would not appear curved but as a plane of finite area; but as we cannot look at it from an elliptic 3-space, this is not entirely convincing— the less so as it has to some extent become customary to speak of the characteristic constant of the space as its "curvature," because of its appearance from a Euclidean higher space. In reality this is incorrect, as the elliptic 2-space and the lines in it are not curved inherently and their appearance to us as sphere and as circle is merely the appearance of their relation to the Euclidean 3-space from which we view them. As already brought out, the same 2-space and its lines would appear differently curved from a different 3-space, and would not appear curved from a 3-space of the same characteristic constant as that of the 2-space. Unfortunately we have no such elliptic 3-space. However, the idea can be grasped by viewing an elliptic 2-space under conditions where we do not have a Euclidean 3-space from which to look at the 2-space, but where we view the elliptic 2-space by itself, in comparison with a Euclidean 2-space. We see then that there is nothing curved about the former any more than about the latter.

Mathematical space is a dimensional continuous manifold. The elements of it, while we may call them points, have nothing to do with the physical point—that is, the position in physical space—but may be any continuously changeable quantity, for instance, color, composition of a gas mixture, forces in physical space.[1] Physical space is a

[1] Thus for instance, all the forces in physical space form a six-dimensional manifold.

three-dimensional manifold with the point—that is, the location in space—as element, and therefore when comparing it with mathematical space we generally choose the point as the element of mathematical space. This, however, is not essential, and we could just as well conceive of a mathematical space with the line as element or the plane as element, etc. This is commonly done in projective geometry, and it leads to valuable results.

Suppose, then, we have a Euclidean plane or 2-space of zero characteristic E; that is, the two-dimensional manifold of points p and lines L contained in the plane E. From a point O outside of E we can project E. Every point p of E then is projected by a line through O (usually called a "ray"). $l = Op$, and every line L of E is projected from O by a plane $P = OL$. To the points p of E thus correspond the lines or rays l through O, and to the lines L of E correspond the planes P through O. All these lines l and planes P through O thus form a two-dimensional continuous manifold—that is, a 2-space—which corresponds element for element to the points and lines p and L of the Euclidean 2-space E.

Such a 2-space, consisting of all the lines and planes through the point O, is called a "bundle." Every figure consisting of points and lines in the Euclidean plane E is projected by and gives a figure consisting of lines and planes in the bundle O; every angle between two lines in E is projected by an angle between the two corresponding planes in O; every triangle in E is projected by a triside in O, that is, a three-sided pyramid; every curve in E by a cone in O, etc., and to the geometry of the plane E thus corresponds a geometry of the bundle O, by projection. We can directly read off the theorems of the geometry of the bundle O from the theorems of the geometry of the plane E by saying, in the bundle, "line" or "ray" for "point" in the plane, and saying in the bundle O "plane" for "line" in plane E. Thus, for instance, the theorem of plane geometry of Fig. 25:

"If the three lines connecting corresponding corners of two triangles meet in one point, the three points of intersection of corresponding sides lie in a straight line,"
would be in the geometry of the bundle:
"If the three planes connecting corresponding edges of two trisides intersect in a line, the three lines of intersection of corresponding side planes lie in a plane."
The latter is derived from the former by projecting it from point O.

Two congruent triangles in E are projected by two trisides in O, but these two trisides are not congruent. Two congruent trisides in O (that is, two trisides of which the one can be moved into coincidence with the other) give two triangles in E, but these two triangles are not congruent. Thus, while all the theorems dealing with the relative position of the elements—points and lines in E, lines and planes in O—remain the same in the two 2-spaces, the Euclidean plane E and the bundle O, the theorems dealing with metric relations, such as congruent, equal, etc., do not transfer. That is, the geometry which E and O have in common is the geometry of position, or projective geometry (column 4 on page 74), but not the metric geometry. In other words, the characteristic constant of the 2-space O is different from that of the plane E.

"Length" or "distance" we call the part of the line between two points. To the line L of E corresponds the plane P projecting the line L from O, and to the two points p_1 and p_2 on the line L in E correspond two lines l_1 and l_2 in the plane P (the lines projecting the two points from O). To the distance, as the part p_1p_2 of the line L in E, thus corresponds in O the part of the plane P between the lines l_1l_2; that is, the angle l_1l_2. Thus "distance" or "length" in our new 2-space, the bundle O, is the angle between the two lines or rays, which are the "points" or elements of the 2-space O.

The length of the straight line L in the Euclidean plane E is infinite. That is, starting from a point p of this line L

and moving along this line in one direction, I have to go into infinity and then come back from infinity on the other side of the line before I again reach point p.   If in the "line" of the bundle O—that is, the plane P which corresponds to the line L of E—I start from a "point"—that is, the ray or line l corresponding to the point p of E—and follow the motion of p along line L, the corresponding ray l moves through the plane P; that is, turns around the point O. But while the point p on L in the plane E traverses an infinite distance before it returns, the corresponding ray l on P in O returns after one complete revolution; that is, after traversing the angle 2π.   Since the "length" in our 2-space O is measured by the angle, it thus follows that the "length" of the straight line P in the 2-space O is 2π. In other words, the length of the straight line in 2-space O is finite, and this 2-space, the bundle, thus is an elliptic 2-space.

The length of a straight line in an elliptic 2-space is $2\pi R$, where R is the "radius" of the 2-space, and is given by the characteristic constant $K = 1/R^2$.   As in the bundle O the length of the straight line is 2π, it follows that in this bundle it is $R = 1$; thus $K = 1$.   That is, the bundle O is an elliptic 2-space of characteristic constant or curvature 1.

An area in E, like that of a triangle, is projected from O by a spherical angle.   "Area" or "volume" in the 2-space O thus is measured as a spherical angle.   The total area of E is projected by the total spherical angle at O.   But while the area of E is infinite, the total spherical angle of O— that is, the total area or "volume" of the 2-space—is finite.

Every angle between two lines L_1L_2 in E is projected by an angle between the two planes P_1 and P_2, which correspond to the lines L_1 and L_2.   The angle between the planes of the bundle O differs from the angle between the lines of the plane E, to which it corresponds.   It is larger if the perpendicular form O on to E falls inside of the angle smaller if the perpendicular falls outside of the angle.

Every triangle in E is projected by a triside in O—that is, a three-sided pyramid, which is the "triangle" of the 2-space called the bundle. If the triside and the corresponding triangle are situated so that the perpendicular from O on E falls inside of the triside, then each angle of the triside is larger than the corresponding angle of the triangle, as seen above, and as the sum of the angles in the triangle in E equals 180 degrees, the sum of the angles in the triside is thus larger than 180 degrees. If the triside is situated so that the perpendicular from O on E falls outside of the triside, the bundle O and with it the triside can be turned so that the perpendicular falls inside of it. (The corresponding triangle obviously then has changed in shape and position on E, but the sum of its angles is still 180 degrees.) Thus in any triside the sum of the angles is greater than 180 degrees, and the bundle thus is an elliptic 2-space.

A curve in the Euclidean plane E gives a cone in the bundle O, and inversely. Suppose we have a circle in the 2-space O; that is, a circular cone. We may move it so that its center line is perpendicular to E. It then will project on E by a circle, and if C is the circumference, r the radius of the circular cone (both in angular measure, as "length" in 2-space O is measured as angle), then from the relation between the circular cone and its projecting circle it follows:

$$C = 2\pi \sin r,$$

and as $\sin r$ always is less than r, it is:

$$C < 2\pi r,$$

and the circumference of the circle is less than π times the diameter, the more so the larger the circle.

The largest circle which can exist in the 2-space O has the radius $\pi/2$, or diameter π, and its circumference is 2π. It is the straight line of the 2-space O. The straight line of the elliptic 2-space O thus can be considered as a circle with radius $\pi/2$, just as the straight line of the Euclidean 2-space can be considered as a circle with radius ∞.

Thus we have here, by projection from a Euclidean plane E, produced an elliptic 2-space of unit curvature, in the bundle O, by using the ray—that is, the line—as element instead of the point, and thus have a chance to study the characteristics of the elliptic 2-space on the bundle O, with the advantage that now we do not look at it from a higher space of different characteristic constant, but from an entirely unrelated space; that is, a space of different elements. We see now that in this 2-space O, while it is elliptic, of characteristic constant or "curvature" 1, there is nothing curved about it. Its straight line is the plane P. It has a finite length 2π, but there is nothing curved about P, and we see thus that while the elliptic 2-space in the Euclidean 3-space appears curved, as sphere, and the straight lines in it appear curved, as circles, this is not a feature of the elliptic 2-space, but of its relation to the Euclidean 3-space, since when unrelated to an Euclidean 3-space there is nothing curved in the elliptic 2-space, as the bundle O.

In the Euclidean plane E we have parallels. But two parallels of E project from O by two planes as "lines" of the bundle, which intersect in a line or ray—that is, a "point" of O—and this is just as finite and real as any other. Any two planes of O intersect; thus there are no parallels in O. The infinitely distant points of E project from O by rays, which are parallel to the plane E, but in O are just like any other rays, are finite. Thus there is no infinity in the elliptic 2-space O.

The elliptic 2-space O is finite; the length of any straight line in it is 2π; its total volume or area is 4π. And still there is nothing outside or beyond it in 2-space, but it is all the space, and so shows how a finite volume—or "area" in 2-space, here measured by the spherical angle from O— can fill all the space.

In many respects this elliptic 2-space, derived by using the line or "ray" as element instead of the point, is more convenient and illustrative than the point space on the spherical surface for realizing the characteristics of elliptic space.

I. PROJECTIVE GEOMETRY

By eliminating the metric axioms we limit the general geometry, or projective geometry, to mere relations of position, but exclude all theorems dealing with equality, congruence, proportionality and similarity, with numerical relations and measurement, with parallels and the effect of infinitely distant elements, as the distinction between ellipsis, hyperbola, circle and parabola, etc. It might be thought that very little is left then for consideration, and a few theorems of the general or projective geometry may therefore be given to illustrate the wide and interesting field of geometrical research outside of the metric axioms.

Theorems of geometry of position, or projective geometry, which hold on the sphere and pseudo-sphere, and in the bundle as well as in the Euclidean plane, are:

1. If the three lines connecting corresponding corners of two triangles meet in a point, then the three points of intersection of corresponding sides of these two triangles lie on a straight line.

This theorem is shown in Fig. 25 on a Euclidean plane, in Fig. 26 on corrugation as Euclidean 2-space, in Fig. 27 on a sphere, and in Fig. 28 on a spindle as elliptic 2-space. We have mentioned it already in the bundle as elliptic 2-space with a different element.

2. In a plane (Fig. 29) are given two lines, L_1 and L_2, and three points, p_0, p_1, p_2, outside of these two lines. From the point p_0 lines are drawn intersecting the lines L_1 and L_2 in the respective points a_1 and a_2, b_1 and b_2, c_1 and c_2, etc. Then the points of intersection, a of the lines p_1a_1 and p_2a_2, b of p_1b_1 and p_2b_2, c of p_1c_1 and p_2c_2, etc., lie on a conic section. On this conic also lie the points p_1 and p_2, the point of intersection q of the lines L_1 and L_2 with each other, and the points of intersection s_1 of the line L_1 with p_0p_2 and s_2 of L_2 with p_0p_1.

It is interesting to note that the conic is an element of projective geometry, defined as a curve of second order; that is, by the feature that a straight line can intersect it in a maximum of two points. The classifications of the conic, however, are no part of projective geometry, as they are

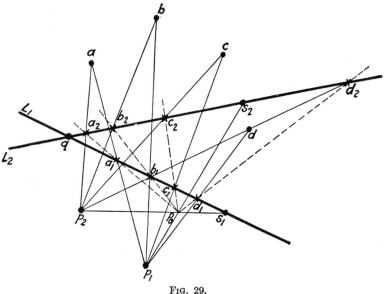

Fig. 29.

made by its relation to infinity and therefore are metric in character: The hyperbola has two infinitely distant points, the parabola has one infinitely distant point, the ellipsis has no infinitely distant point; that is, its two infinitely distant points are imaginary, and the circle is the ellipsis in which the two imaginary infinitely distant points are at right angles to each other. This classification of conics applies only in the Euclidean plane, but not on the sphere or in the bundle, as in the elliptic space there is no infinity.

3. If from a point p (Fig. 30) two lines are drawn intersecting a conic (as, for instance, a circle) in the points a_1 and a_2 and b_1 and b_2 respectively, and the points of intersection, p' of a_1b_1 and a_2b_2 and p'' of a_1b_2 and a_2b_1, are connected by a straight line P, and p_1 and p_2 are the points of

intersection of this line P with the conic, then pp_1 and pp_2 are tangents of the conic at the point p_1 and p_2 respectively. The line P is called the *polar* of the point p.

Any line through p intersects the polar P in a point p_0, which is the fourth harmonic point to p with respect to the two intersections of pp_0 with the conic.

If P_1 and P_2 are the polars of the two points p_1 and p_2 with regard to a conic, then the line connecting the points

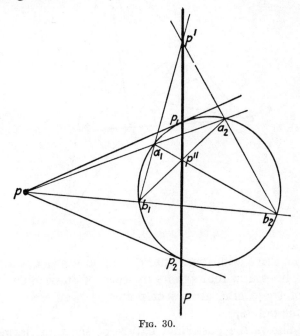

Fig. 30.

p_1 and p_2 is the polar of the point of intersection of P_1 and P_2, and inversely.

This gives a means to construct the tangents on a conic; for instance, a circle.

As has been seen, the harmonic relation between four points exists in projective geometry. This shows that this relation, while usually considered as metric and introduced as such, in its nature is not a metric relation but a positional relation.

4. If we have, in Fig. 31, four points *a*, *b*, *c*, *d*, in a plane, and draw the six lines through them, *ab*, *ac*, *ad*, *bc*, *bd*, *cd*, and denote the three additional points of intersection of these six lines by *e* = *ab*, *cd*; *f* = *ac*, *bd*; *g* = *ad*, *bc*, and

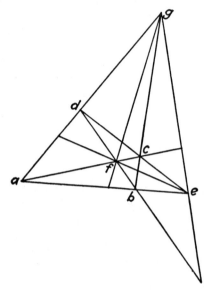

Fig. 31.

draw the three additional lines *ef*, *eg* and *fg*, we get a total of nine lines and four points on each of these nine lines. Each of these nine groups of points is composed of four harmonic points.

This shows the positional nature of the four harmonic points.

J. THE METRIC AXIOM AND THE LAW OF GRAVITATION

In Lecture I, and more completely in Lecture III, we have seen that the laws of the motion in a gravitational field are identical with the laws of inertial motion in an accelerated system, and that the former—that is, the law of gravitation—can be derived as the equations of mathematical transformation to an accelerated system without making any assumption on the physical nature of the gravitational force. In this manner Einstein has derived his law of gravitation. This transformation, however, which leads to the law of gravitation, is not entirely without arbitrary assumption, as it would appear to be at first. The law of gravitation is a metric relation. We have seen, however, in the preceding that metric relations do not exist in general space, but space in general is projective, involving only relations of position, and that a particular characteristic of space, a metric axiom, is necessary to give relations of size and measurement between figures in a space, or between two spaces, such as the elliptic space of the gravitational field and the Euclidean characteristic of fieldless space. Einstein's derivation of the law of gravitation, however, assumes the possibility of a mathematical transformation to the accelerated system, which is of metric nature; that is, assumes the existence of metric relations and therefore requires the selection of a metric axiom. Any axiom which establishes metric relations would obviously fulfill the conditions of permitting the transformation to the accelerated system, and thus give a law of gravitation. Thus many different forms of the law of gravitation could be derived, since different forms of metric axioms could be chosen and the form of the metric axiom is arbitrary. Einstein chose the metric axiom which gives the simplest formulation of the physical and mathematical laws. This is it: "Whatever may be the characteristic or curvature of the space, and however it may vary from point to point or remain constant, an element of space—that is, an infinitely small part of it—is plane or Euclidean."

The general geometry of space (whether 2-space, that is, plane geometry, or 3-space, that is, solid geometry) is projective or non-metrical; that is, it deals with problems of position only, and its space is merely a dimensional continuous manifold, as discussed before. Metric relations, such as equality of length, area, volume, congruence, the relation of smaller or larger, proportionality, the distinction between finite and infinitely distant, etc., are foreign to general space, but require an additional property of space beyond that of being a continuous manifold, namely, the property, that measurement—that is, comparison of sizes of figures—can be carried out.   Measurement is carried out by bringing figures into coincidence—that is, the measuring rule with the length to be measured, the area to be measured with the unit area used as measure, the triangles which are to be proven as congruent with each other, etc.   To make this possible it is necessary that figures can be moved in space without changing.   Obviously, if moving a figure, as a triangle, would change its size, we could not prove or discuss the equality or congruence of two figures by moving one into coincidence with the other, since when we moved it it would not be the same figure any more.   Metric space is, therefore, characterized, in distinction to general space, by the additional axiom:

"Figures can be moved in space without change of their size or of the size of their component parts."

This metric axiom leads to the condition that the characteristic, or curvature, of the space must be constant.   Thus there are only three spaces in which complete metric relations are possible, the Euclidean or plane, the elliptic and the hyperbolic space.   Complete metric relations, such as congruence of figures, etc., exist only within a space of constant curvature or between different spaces of the same curvature, as between the plane and the conical surface (zero 2-space) or between the sphere and the surface of a spindle of the same curvature as the sphere.   They do not exist, for instance, between the plane and the sphere— 2-spaces of different curvature.   A triangle in the plane and a triangle on a sphere can never be congruent and can never be made to coincide.   If the sides of the two triangles were equal and I try to make them coincide, I have to stretch or contract the area of one to make it fit the other, and this changes its area, its angles, etc., so that it is not the same triangle any more.   The same thing is true with two spherical triangles of different curvature, as, for instance, located at two different parts of an egg-shaped surface, a 2-space of varying positive curvature. The metric relation of congruence, or proportionality, etc., does not exist in a space of varying curvature, as figures cannot be moved to bring them into coincidence without changing their shape by stretching or contracting.

It is not possible, therefore, to represent an elliptic 2-space—like the surface of the earth—on a plane 2-space—as in a plane map—without distorting the dimensions, getting the different parts out of proportion with each other.

Nevertheless, a partial metric relation is possible in spaces of varying curvature or between spaces of different curvature. For instance, we measure the length of a curve, like the circumference of a circle, by comparing it with a straight line.[1] We measure the area of a sphere or a part of it (as the surface of the earth or that of a country) by comparing it with a flat or plane unit area—for instance, a square mile —though this can be done only indirectly and there is no possibility of physically carrying out such measurement, as we can never make a flat unit area coincide with a curved surface or a part of it. We can do it, however, by comparing the two, the curved line and the straight line, or the curved area and the flat unit area, element by element. If we desired to measure the circumference of a circle three feet in diameter by a straight rule one foot in length, we should get very inaccurate results, as a rule one foot in length cannot be made to coincide with the curved periphery of the circle. If, however, we were to use a straight rule one inch in length, we should get much more accurate results in measuring a circle three feet in diameter, as the

---

[1] It appears to us obvious now that the length of a curved line can be measured, that is, compared with the length of a straight measuring rod; but this is not at all so obvious, and it was a matter of serious discussion by the great mathematicians of ancient time whether there could be such a thing as a "measurement" of the circumference of a circle.

one-inch straight rule could be made almost to coincide with a part of the periphery.   The shorter the straight rule we use, the more accurately it will coincide with the curved periphery of the circle and the more accurate will be the measurement, and if it were possible to use an infinitely short rule in measuring the length of a curved line, we should get perfect accuracy.   This means, in other words, that the shorter a part of a curved line is the straighter it is, and that an infinitely short part of a curved line is straight.

The same applies with areas or surfaces.   The smaller a part of a curved surface is the planer it is, and an infinitely small part of a curved surface is plane.

This makes it possible to measure the length of curved lines, the area of curved surfaces, the volume of curved spaces, etc.   The characteristics are:

"A piece of a curved line is the straighter the shorter it is, and an infinitely short piece of a curved line is straight."

"A piece of a curved surface is the planer the smaller it is, and an infinitely small piece of a curved surface is plane."

"A piece of a curved space is the planer the smaller it is, and an infinitely small piece of a curved (or non-Euclidean) space is plane, that is, Euclidean."

This, however, is not an inherent property of space.   It does not hold for the general or non-metric space, but it is a special ·condition imposed upon space.   It is a metric axiom, the adoption of which gives to space characteristics beyond those of general space, namely, the property that measurements can be made in space.

For instance, at the point of the cone, or at the singular line of the pseudo-sphere, this axiom does not hold, and no matter how small a piece at the point of the cone or the singular line of the pseudo-sphere we take, it never is plane or Euclidean.   This condition that the space element is Euclidean applies to all spaces of constant curvature, and therefore, in describing the characteristics of these spaces, we said, for instance, referring to elliptic space: "The sum of the angles in a triangle is greater than 180 degrees, the more so the larger the triangle." In an infinitely small triangle of elliptic space the sum of the angles is 180 degrees, because an infinitely small piece of elliptic space is Euclidean.

However, the spaces of constant curvature are more special than the space with the Euclidean element. For instance, an egg-shaped surface does not have constant curvature, but its element is Euclidean.

We thus have here three successive gradations of the conception of mathematical space:

1. The general space, as a continuous manifold, in which a geometry of position exists, but no metric geometry.

2. The differential metric space, that is, the general space with the differential metric axiom added, the axiom that an element of the space is Euclidean. This permits those metric relations which can be derived by segregation into elements (line elements, surface elements, etc.) and permits measurement of lengths and areas, but not comparison of figures, such as congruence, as motion of figures in the space is not possible without change.

3. The completely metric space—that is, the differential metric space with the integral metric axiom added, the axiom that figures can be moved in space without change of shape. This gives the space of constant curvature, Euclidean, elliptic or hyperbolic.

The differentially metric space, established by the axiom that the element of the space is plane or Euclidean, is not the most general metric space, but the most general metric space would be established by the differential metric axiom that all the elements of the space are of the same characteristic. But whether this characteristic of the space element is Euclidean or of any other form is arbitrary. That is:

2_0. The general differential metric space is the general space with the axiom added that all the elements of the space have the same characteristic. That is, if ds is a line element and dx_i an element of the coördinate x_i (where

$i = 1$ and 2 for 2-space, 1, 2 and 3 for 3-space, $1.2 - n$ for n-space), it is:

$$ds^2 = f^2(dx_i) = \text{independent of } x_i;$$

that is, ds^2 is a constant quadratic function of the coördinate element dx_i.

For the special differential metric space, in which the elements are Euclidean, it is:

$$ds^2 = \Sigma dx_i{}^2,$$

while in general, for differential metric 3-space, it is:

$$ds^2 = g_1 dx_1{}^2 + g_2 dx_2{}^2 + g_3 dx_3{}^2 + g_{12} dx_1 dx_2 + g_{23} dx_2 dx_3 + g_{31} dx_3 dx_1.$$

As the elliptic space of the gravitational field and the Euclidean space of fieldless regions have a different curvature, complete metric relations, such as congruence of figures in the two spaces, cannot exist between them. Since, however, both spaces are differentially metric spaces—that is, their elements are Euclidean—such metric relations as exist in differentially metric spaces—that is, comparison of the length of lines, areas of surfaces, volumes of bodies—exist between elliptic and Euclidean space. In the transformation to an accelerated system, which leads to his formulation of the law of gravitation, Einstein therefore makes the assumption of the existence of the differentially metric axiom. This is necessary, as without it no metric relations could be established, but nevertheless it is an arbitrary feature, justified only by the simplicity of the results.

K. VISUAL APPEARANCE OF CURVED SPACE

The distance of an object we estimate by the difference in the direction in which we see it from the two eyes. Thus, if, in Fig. 32, O is an object and A_1 and A_2 the two eyes, the difference in the two lines of sight A_1O and A_2O gives us the distance of O. If O is further away, the lines A_1O and A_2O differ less in direction, and finally, when O is

infinitely far away, the two lines of sight A_1O and A_2O
have the same direction. That an object is infinitely distant (that is, very far distant) we thus recognize by the

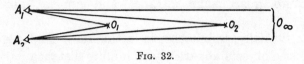

Fɪɢ. 32.

two lines of sight from our eyes to the object having the
same direction.

This is in Euclidean space.

How would elliptic and hyperbolic space look to us?

In elliptic space there is no infinite distance, and the
straight line is finite in length. Thus, if there were no
obstructions and no light-absorbing medium, the line of
sight from the eye should return into itself; that is, everywhere where the view is free we should see the back of our
head covering all open space—because all lines of vision,
in whatever direction we look, return into themselves
through the back of our head. However, this is meaningless in our universe, since, though finite, it is so enormously
large—the length of the straight line being equal to about
400,000,000 light-years—that light would have been
absorbed long before it had completed the closed path.

In elliptic space there is no infinite distance and the
straight line is finite in length. We would estimate the
distance of an object O in the same manner as in Fig. 32,
by the difference in the direction of the two lines of vision
from the two eyes to the object, and the further the object
is away the less is the difference in this direction, until
finally, when the object is at the distance of one-quarter
the length of the line (one quadrant of the circle as which
the straight line of the elliptic space appears to us from a
higher Euclidean space), the two lines of vision A_1O and
A_2O have the same direction; that is, the object O appears
at infinite distance. Thus, though elliptic space is finite
in extent, every object at a quarter-line length from our

eyes appears infinitely distant. When we move toward it, it comes into finite distance, and finally we reach it in a finite distance, while other objects beyond it now have come into quarter-line distance and appear infinitely distant.

Thus, visually, infinity exists in the finite elliptic space, and we see objects apparently at infinite distance, but can reach them in finite distance.

In the hyperbolic space each line L (Fig. 33) has two parallels L_1 and L_2 through a point P—that is, two lines

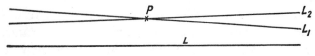

Fig. 33.

which intersect L at infinity—and these two parallels L_1 and L_2 make an angle L_1PL_2 with each other. Thus L_1 differs in direction from L at the point P, though parallel, that is, intersecting it at infinity. Thus, if I look at a receding object O in hyperbolic space, the difference in the direction of the two lines of vision from the two eyes, A_1O and A_2O (Fig. 32) gets the less the further the object is away. But even when the object O is infinitely far away, the two lines of sight toward it still differ in direction by the angle by which two parallels differ in hyperbolic space, and the object therefore appears to be at finite distance. Visually there is no infinite distance in hyperbolic space, but all objects appear at finite distance, even infinitely distant objects. But such infinitely distant objects, though appearing at finite distance to the view, never get any nearer, no matter how far we move toward them. We may estimate their (apparent) distance and move toward them by this distance and more, and still they appear just as far, at the same apparently finite distance. (This reminds us of the similar characteristic of the velocity of light c in the relativity theory, which is finite, $c = 3 \times 10^{10}$ cm., but still inapproachable, as no combination or addition of lesser velocities can ever add to a sum equal to *c*.)

Helmholtz has shown that we can get a view of hyperbolic space by looking at our space through a large, slightly concave lens which covers both eyes.

We thus find:

Euclidean space is infinite in extent, appears infinite visually and is unbounded.

Elliptic space is finite in extent, but appears infinite visually and is unbounded. Objects at a quarter-line distance appear infinitely distant.

Hyperbolic space is infinite in extent, but appears finite visually and is unbounded.

L. THE TWO-DIMENSIONAL ANALOGUE OF THE UNIVERSE, AND THE MATHEMATICAL CONCEPTION OF IT

The relativity theory has reconfirmed the law of conservation of energy, but has denied the law of conservation of matter by showing matter as kinetic energy, m_0c^2, where c = velocity of light and m_0 is a constant. Mass then is represented by:

$$m = \frac{m_0c^2 + E}{\sqrt{1 - \dfrac{v^2}{c^2}}}$$

where v is the relative velocity and E the non-kinetic energy of the body.

The constancy of the mass then is approximate only as long as v is small compared with c and E small compared with m_0c^2. This is the case at all but ionic velocities and energies.

The gravitational field of matter, then, is of the character of an accelerated system, and in the gravitational field the laws of the Euclidean geometry cease to hold and space shows a positive or elliptic curvature.

Space, then, and its characteristic or curvature are functions of matter and thus of energy. That is, space is plane or Euclidean in the absence of matter and becomes elliptic or positively curved in the presence of matter, the more so the larger the amount of matter present; that is, the greater the gravitational field, as we say.

The universe, as we know, consists of isolated huge masses, the fixed stars, which are surrounded by their gravitational fields, but separated from each other by enormous distances of empty or practically empty and therefore essentially Euclidean space. At the masses of the fixed stars the curvature of the universe thus is positive; in their gravitational fields it gradually tapers down to zero in the fieldless space between the fixed stars. Geometrically, we may thus picture for ourselves a two-dimensional analogy of our universe by replacing the fixed stars with very shallow spherical segments—positive 2-space—which continue as very shallow conical surfaces—the gravitational fields—into the flat Euclidean planes of fieldless space, as shown in the reproduction of such a model in Fig. 34.[1] As has been seen, owing to the curvature of the spherical segments (the masses), if we traverse the model in a straight line, we gradually curve in a direction at right angles to the plane of the model—that is, into the third dimension— so that we return to our starting point after passing about twelve masses. This shows how the existence of positively curved regions (masses) makes the total universe of finite extent.

However, this analogy of a two-dimensional model with our universe must not be carried too far, as it is deficient in an essential feature. In the 2-space we have either positive or negative or zero curvature, depending on whether the two radii of curvature of the surface are in the same direction or in opposite direction, or whether one is zero. In

---

[1] This Fig. 34 shows the two-dimensional analogy of our universe about one million times exaggerated. That is, the actual curvature is about one-millionth as much as shown, or, instead of twelve, about twelve million masses are passed before a straight line returns into itself in the physical universe.

3-space, however, there are three radii of curvature, and combinations exist which have no analogy in 2-space and therefore cannot be illustrated by analogy with it. This limits the completeness of the 2-space analogies with 3-space relations, so that the preceding can be considered only as giving a rather crude conception of the 3-space characteristics.

Physical space, we have seen, is not a space of constant curvature, but of a curvature which varies from point to point with the distribution of matter. From what we have discussed, therefore, it follows that the metric axioms do not rigidly hold in physical space, and figures cannot be moved in space without stretching or contracting when passing from a point of space to a point of different curvature. Measurements and dimensional relations, therefore, are not rigidly possible in physical space, and strictly, we cannot speak of the length or the size of a body, as we cannot measure it by bringing the measure to it, because the length and shape of the measure change when it is moved through space. Thus length and size are not fixed properties of a body, but depend on the conditions under which they are determined, and this brings us back to the conclusions of the first lecture on the relativity of length and time.

Instead of the physical conception of mass as a kinetic energy which causes a curvature, a deformation or "kink" in space, we may start from the mathematical side and consider mass and its gravitational field as the manifestation or physical representation of a curvature of space. We may consider physical space as varying in curvature between zero and positive values. In other words, space, though in general of zero curvature, or Euclidean, contains singular points, or rather regions of positive curvature, which we call "masses." In a region surrounding a region of positive curvature or "mass" the curvature of the space gradually changes from the positive values in the mass to zero at distance from the mass, and such a region we call the gravitational field of the mass. Energy then becomes space curvature, and the characteristic constant of space is the measure of energy.

The limitations of this mathematical conception of the physical universe are that the electromagnetic energy and the electromagnetic field do not yet satisfactorily fit into it.

INSTRUCTIONS FOR OBSERVING THE ILLUS-
TRATIONS STEREOSCOPICALLY

By a little practice, one can throw these illustrations into stereoscopic vision without the use of a stereoscope. This is done by the use of a black cardboard barrier to constrain the left eye to see only the left image, and the right eye, the right. Hold a piece of black cardboard, 3½ by 8 inches, perpendicular to the page, with the 3½ inch end resting on the page midway between the two images. Hold the page so that both images are equally illuminated and no shadows on them, and with the end of the cardboard touching the nose and forehead. You will thus see only one image, which at first may appear unsteady and somewhat blurred, both because the image is too close for the eyes properly to adjust themselves in focus, and also the angle at which the eyes are now required to set themselves is unnatural. Slowly move the page and cardboard (the latter held always perpendicular to the page) away from the face, concentrating persistently on this image and on some single feature of the image, such as a line intersection, until the page is at the ordinary reading distance from the eyes. The lines will then be in focus, the single image will stand out in perfect stereoscopic effect, and attention can now be turned from the particular feature to the image as a whole. The surface of the ball and the lines on it will appear curved, as in an actual sphere, and the corrugations of the paper surfaces will stand out in relief, so that the proper curvature of the lines can be observed.

However, to get stereoscopic vision, it is necessary that both eyes have the same focal length, or to wear glasses correcting for the same focal length.

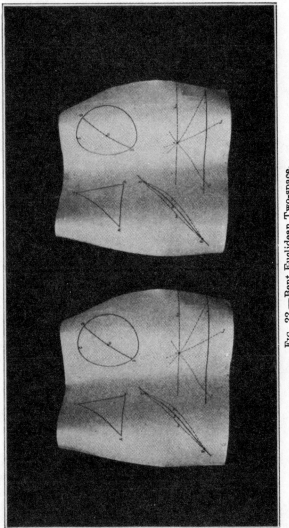

FIG. 22.—Bent Euclidean Two-space.

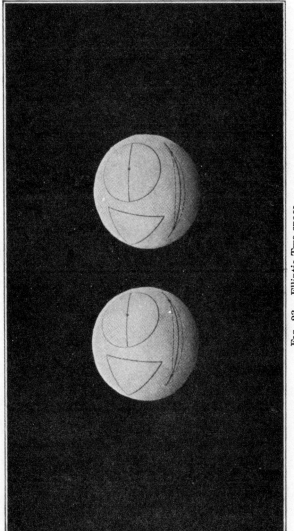

Fig. 23.—Elliptic Two-space.

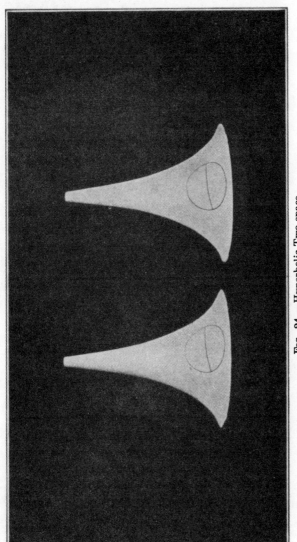

Fig. 24.—Hyperbolic Two-space.

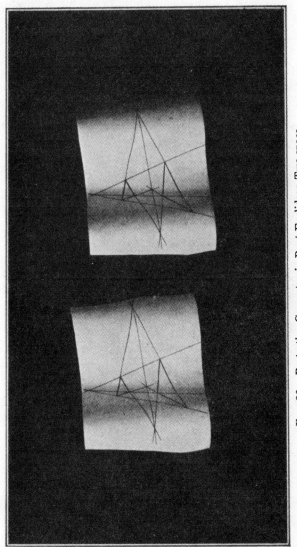

Fig. 26.—Projective Geometry in Bent Euclidean Two-space.

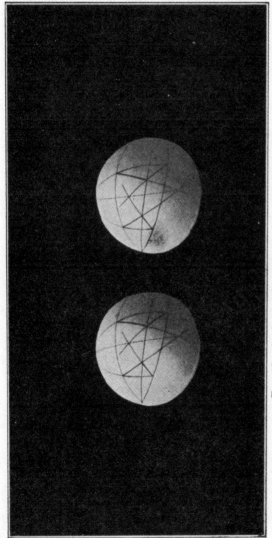

Fig. 27.—Projective Geometry in Elliptic Two-space.

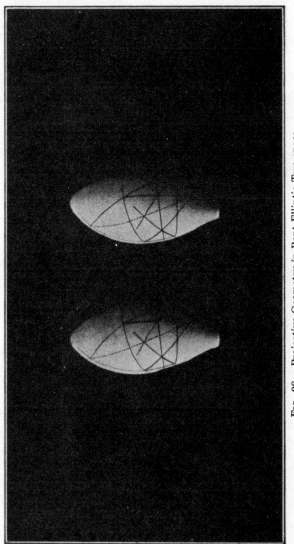

Fig. 28.—Projective Geometry in Bent Elliptic Two-space.

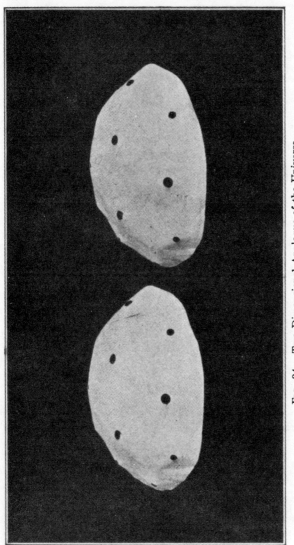

Fig. 34.—Two-Dimensional Analogue of the Universe.

INDEX

CATALOGUE OF DOVER BOOKS

PHYSICS

General physics

FOUNDATIONS OF PHYSICS, R. B. Lindsay & H. Margenau. Excellent bridge between semipopular works & technical treatises. A discussion of methods of physical description, construction of theory; valuable for physicist with elementary calculus who is interested in ideas that give meaning to data, tools of modern physics. Contents include symbolism, mathematical equations; space & time foundations of mechanics; probability; physics & continua; electron theory; special & general relativity; quantum mechanics; causality. "Thorough and yet not overdetailed. Unreservedly recommended," NATURE (London). Unabridged, corrected edition. List of recommended readings. 35 illustrations. xi + 537pp. 5⅜ x 8.
S377 Paperbound **$2.75**

FUNDAMENTAL FORMULAS OF PHYSICS, ed. by D. H. Menzel. Highly useful, fully inexpensive reference and study text, ranging from simple to highly sophisticated operations. Mathematics integrated into text—each chapter stands as short textbook of field represented. Vol. 1: Statistics, Physical Constants, Special Theory of Relativity, Hydrodynamics, Aerodynamics, Boundary Value Problems in Math. Physics; Viscosity, Electromagnetic Theory, etc. Vol. 2: Sound, Acoustics, Geometrical Optics, Electron Optics, High-Energy Phenomena, Magnetism, Biophysics, much more. Index. Total of 800pp. 5⅜ x 8.
Vol. 1 S595 Paperbound **$2.00**
Vol. 2 S596 Paperbound **$2.00**

MATHEMATICAL PHYSICS, D. H. Menzel. Thorough one-volume treatment of the mathematical techniques vital for classic mechanics, electromagnetic theory, quantum theory, and relativity. Written by the Harvard Professor of Astrophysics for junior, senior, and graduate courses, it gives clear explanations of all those aspects of function theory, vectors, matrices, dyadics, tensors, partial differential equations, etc., necessary for the understanding of the various physical theories. Electron theory, relativity, and other topics seldom presented appear here in considerable detail. Scores of definitions, conversion factors, dimensional constants, etc. "More detailed than normal for an advanced text . . . excellent set of sections on Dyadics, Matrices, and Tensors," JOURNAL OF THE FRANKLIN INSTITUTE. Index. 193 problems, with answers. x + 412pp. 5⅜ x 8.
S56 Paperbound **$2.00**

THE SCIENTIFIC PAPERS OF J. WILLARD GIBBS. All the published papers of America's outstanding theoretical scientist (except for "Statistical Mechanics" and "Vector Analysis"). Vol I (thermodynamics) contains one of the most brilliant of all 19th-century scientific papers—the 300-page "On the Equilibrium of Heterogeneous Substances," which founded the science of physical chemistry, and clearly stated a number of highly important natural laws for the first time; 8 other papers complete the first volume. Vol II includes 2 papers on dynamics, 8 on vector analysis and multiple algebra, 5 on the electromagnetic theory of light, and 6 miscellaneous papers. Biographical sketch by H. A. Bumstead. Total of xxxvi + 718pp. 5⅝ x 8⅜.
S721 Vol I Paperbound **$2.50**
S722 Vol II Paperbound **$2.00**
The set **$4.50**

BASIC THEORIES OF PHYSICS, Peter Gabriel Bergmann. Two-volume set which presents a critical examination of important topics in the major subdivisions of classical and modern physics. The first volume is concerned with classical mechanics and electrodynamics: mechanics of mass points, analytical mechanics, matter in bulk, electrostatics and magnetostatics, electromagnetic interaction, the field waves, special relativity, and waves. The second volume (Heat and Quanta) contains discussions of the kinetic hypothesis, physics and statistics, stationary ensembles, laws of thermodynamics, early quantum theories, atomic spectra, probability waves, quantization in wave mechanics, approximation methods, and abstract quantum theory. A valuable supplement to any thorough course or text.
Heat and Quanta: Index. 8 figures. x + 300pp. 5⅜ x 8½.
S968 Paperbound **$2.00**
Mechanics and Electrodynamics: Index. 14 figures. vii + 280pp. 5⅜ x 8½.
S969 Paperbound **$1.75**

THEORETICAL PHYSICS, A. S. Kompaneyets. One of the very few thorough studies of the subject in this price range. Provides advanced students with a comprehensive theoretical background. Especially strong on recent experimentation and developments in quantum theory. Contents: Mechanics (Generalized Coordinates, Lagrange's Equation, Collision of Particles, etc.), Electrodynamics (Vector Analysis, Maxwell's equations, Transmission of Signals, Theory of Relativity, etc.), Quantum Mechanics (the Inadequacy of Classical Mechanics, the Wave Equation, Motion in a Central Field, Quantum Theory of Radiation, Quantum Theories of Dispersion and Scattering, etc.), and Statistical Physics (Equilibrium Distribution of Molecules in an Ideal Gas, Boltzmann statistics, Bose and Fermi Distribution, Thermodynamic Quantities, etc.). Revised to 1961. Translated by George Yankovsky, authorized by Kompaneyets. 137 exercises. 56 figures. 529pp. 5⅜ x 8½.
S972 Paperbound **$2.50**

ANALYTICAL AND CANONICAL FORMALISM IN PHYSICS, André Mercier. A survey, in one volume, of the variational principles (the key principles—in mathematical form—from which the basic laws of any one branch of physics can be derived) of the several branches of physical theory, together with an examination of the relationships among them. Contents: the Lagrangian Formalism, Lagrangian Densities, Canonical Formalism, Canonical Form of Electrodynamics, Hamiltonian Densities, Transformations, and Canonical Form with Vanishing Jacobian Determinant. Numerous examples and exercises. For advanced students, teachers, etc. 6 figures. Index. viii + 222pp. 5⅜ x 8½.
S1077 Paperbound **$1.75**

HYDRODYNAMICS, H. Dryden, F. Murnaghan, Harry Bateman. Published by the National Research Council in 1932 this enormous volume offers a complete coverage of classical hydrodynamics. Encyclopedic in quality. Partial contents: physics of fluids, motion, turbulent flow, compressible fluids, motion in 1, 2, 3 dimensions; viscous fluids rotating, laminar motion, resistance of motion through viscous fluid, eddy viscosity, hydraulic flow in channels of various shapes, discharge of gases, flow past obstacles, etc. Bibliography of over 2,900 items. Indexes. 23 figures. 634pp. 5⅜ x 8.   S303 Paperbound **$2.75**

Mechanics, dynamics, thermodynamics, elasticity

MECHANICS, J. P. Den Hartog. Already a classic among introductory texts, the M.I.T. professor's lively and discursive presentation is equally valuable as a beginner's text, an engineering student's refresher, or a practicing engineer's reference. Emphasis in this highly readable text is on illuminating fundamental principles and showing how they are embodied in a great number of real engineering and design problems: trusses, loaded cables, beams, jacks, hoists, etc. Provides advanced material on relative motion and gyroscopes not usual in introductory texts. "Very thoroughly recommended to all those anxious to improve their real understanding of the principles of mechanics." MECHANICAL WORLD. Index. List of equations. 334 problems, all with answers. Over 550 diagrams and drawings. ix + 462pp. 5⅜ x 8.
S754 Paperbound **$2.00**

THEORETICAL MECHANICS: AN INTRODUCTION TO MATHEMATICAL PHYSICS, J. S. Ames, F. D. Murnaghan. A mathematically rigorous development of theoretical mechanics for the advanced student, with constant practical applications. Used in hundreds of advanced courses. An unusually thorough coverage of gyroscopic and baryscopic material, detailed analyses of the Coriolis acceleration, applications of Lagrange's equations, motion of the double pendulum, Hamilton-Jacobi partial differential equations, group velocity and dispersion, etc. Special relativity is also included. 159 problems. 44 figures. ix + 462pp. 5⅜ x 8.
S461 Paperbound **$2.25**

THEORETICAL MECHANICS: STATICS AND THE DYNAMICS OF A PARTICLE, W. D. MacMillan. Used for over 3 decades as a self-contained and extremely comprehensive advanced undergraduate text in mathematical physics, physics, astronomy, and deeper foundations of engineering. Early sections require only a knowledge of geometry; later, a working knowledge of calculus. Hundreds of basic problems, including projectiles to the moon, escape velocity, harmonic motion, ballistics, falling bodies, transmission of power, stress and strain, elasticity, astronomical problems. 340 practice problems plus many fully worked out examples make it possible to test and extend principles developed in the text. 200 figures. xvii + 430pp. 5⅜ x 8.   S467 Paperbound **$2.00**

THEORETICAL MECHANICS: THE THEORY OF THE POTENTIAL, W. D. MacMillan. A comprehensive, well balanced presentation of potential theory, serving both as an introduction and a reference work with regard to specific problems, for physicists and mathematicians. No prior knowledge of integral relations is assumed, and all mathematical material is developed as it becomes necessary. Includes: Attraction of Finite Bodies; Newtonian Potential Function; Vector Fields, Green and Gauss Theorems; Attractions of Surfaces and Lines; Surface Distribution of Matter; Two-Layer Surfaces; Spherical Harmonics; Ellipsoidal Harmonics; etc. "The great number of particular cases . . . should make the book valuable to geophysicists and others actively engaged in practical applications of the potential theory," Review of Scientific Instruments. Index. Bibliography. xiii + 469pp. 5⅜ x 8.   S486 Paperbound **$2.50**

THEORETICAL MECHANICS: DYNAMICS OF RIGID BODIES, W. D. MacMillan. Theory of dynamics of a rigid body is developed, using both the geometrical and analytical methods of instruction. Begins with exposition of algebra of vectors, it goes through momentum principles, motion in space, use of differential equations and infinite series to solve more sophisticated dynamics problems. Partial contents: moments of inertia, systems of free particles, motion parallel to a fixed plane, rolling motion, method of periodic solutions, much more. 82 figs. 199 problems. Bibliography. Indexes. xii + 476pp. 5⅜ x 8.   S641 Paperbound **$2.50**

MATHEMATICAL FOUNDATIONS OF STATISTICAL MECHANICS, A. I. Khinchin. Offering a precise and rigorous formulation of problems, this book supplies a thorough and up-to-date exposition. It provides analytical tools needed to replace cumbersome concepts, and furnishes for the first time a logical step-by-step introduction to the subject. Partial contents: geometry & kinematics of the phase space, ergodic problem, reduction to theory of probability, application of central limit problem, ideal monatomic gas, foundation of thermo-dynamics, dispersion and distribution of sum functions. Key to notations. Index. viii + 179pp. 5⅜ x 8.
S147 Paperbound **$1.50**

ELEMENTARY PRINCIPLES IN STATISTICAL MECHANICS, J. W. Gibbs. Last work of the great Yale mathematical physicist, still one of the most fundamental treatments available for advanced students and workers in the field. Covers the basic principle of conservation of probability of phase, theory of errors in the calculated phases of a system, the contributions of Clausius, Maxwell, Boltzmann, and Gibbs himself, and much more. Includes valuable comparison of statistical mechanics with thermodynamics: Carnot's cycle, mechanical definitions of entropy, etc. xvi + 208pp. 5⅜ x 8.   S707 Paperbound **$1.45**

FOUNDATIONS OF POTENTIAL THEORY, O. D. Kellogg. Based on courses given at Harvard this is suitable for both advanced and beginning mathematicians. Proofs are rigorous, and much material not generally avaliable elsewhere is included. Partial contents: forces of gravity, fields of force, divergence theorem, properties of Newtonian potentials at points of free space, potentials as solutions of Laplace's equations, harmonic functions, electrostatics, electric images, logarithmic potential, etc. One of Grundlehren Series. ix + 384pp. 5⅜ x 8.
S144 Paperbound **$2.00**

THERMODYNAMICS, Enrico Fermi. Unabridged reproduction of 1937 edition. Elementary in treatment; remarkable for clarity, organization. Requires no knowledge of advanced math beyond calculus, only familiarity with fundamentals of thermometry, calorimetry. Partial Contents: Thermodynamic systems; First & Second laws of thermodynamics; Entropy; Thermodynamic potentials: phase rule, reversible electric cell; Gaseous reactions: van't Hoff reaction box, principle of LeChatelier; Thermodynamics of dilute solutions: osmotic & vapor pressures, boiling & freezing points; Entropy constant. Index. 25 problems. 24 illustrations. x + 160pp. 5⅜ x 8.
S361 Paperbound **$1.75**

THE THERMODYNAMICS OF ELECTRICAL PHENOMENA IN METALS and A CONDENSED COLLECTION OF THERMODYNAMIC FORMULAS, P. W. Bridgman. Major work by the Nobel Prizewinner: stimulating conceptual introduction to aspects of the electron theory of metals, giving an intuitive understanding of fundamental relationships concealed by the formal systems of Onsager and others. Elementary mathematical formulations show clearly the fundamental thermodynamical relationships of the electric field, and a complete phenomenological theory of metals is created. This is the work in which Bridgman announced his famous "thermomotive force" and his distinction between "driving" and "working" electromotive force. We have added in this Dover edition the author's long unavailable tables of thermodynamic formulas, extremely valuable for the speed of reference they allow. Two works bound as one. Index. 33 figures. Bibliography. xviii + 256pp. 5⅜ x 8. S723 Paperbound **$1.75**

TREATISE ON THERMODYNAMICS, Max Planck. Based on Planck's original papers this offers a uniform point of view for the entire field and has been used as an introduction for students who have studied elementary chemistry, physics, and calculus. Rejecting the earlier approaches of Helmholtz and Maxwell, the author makes no assumptions regarding the nature of heat, but begins with a few empirical facts, and from these deduces new physical and chemical laws. 3rd English edition of this standard text by a Nobel laureate. xvi + 297pp. 5⅜ x 8.
S219 Paperbound **$1.85**

THE MATHEMATICAL THEORY OF ELASTICITY, A. E. H. Love. A wealth of practical illustration combined with thorough discussion of fundamentals—theory, application, special problems and solutions. Partial Contents: Analysis of Strain & Stress, Elasticity of Solid Bodies, Elasticity of Crystals, Vibration of Spheres, Cylinders, Propagation of Waves in Elastic Solid Media, Torsion, Theory of Continuous Beams, Plates. Rigorous treatment of Volterra's theory of dislocations, 2-dimensional elastic systems, other topics of modern interest. "For years the standard treatise on elasticity," AMERICAN MATHEMATICAL MONTHLY. 4th revised edition. Index. 76 figures. xviii + 643pp. 6⅛ x 9¼.
S174 Paperbound **$3.25**

STRESS WAVES IN SOLIDS, H. Kolsky, Professor of Applied Physics, Brown University. The most readable survey of the theoretical core of current knowledge about the propagation of waves in solids, fully correlated with experimental research. Contents: Part I—Elastic Waves: propagation in an extended plastic medium, propagation in bounded elastic media, experimental investigations with elastic materials. Part II—Stress Waves in Imperfectly Elastic Media: internal friction, experimental investigations of dynamic elastic properties, plastic waves and shock waves, fractures produced by stress waves. List of symbols. Appendix. Supplemented bibliography. 3 full-page plates. 46 figures. x + 213pp. 5⅜ x 8½.
S1098 Paperbound **$1.75**

Relativity, quantum theory, atomic and nuclear physics

SPACE TIME MATTER, Hermann Weyl. "The standard treatise on the general theory of relativity" (Nature), written by a world-renowned scientist, provides a deep clear discussion of the logical coherence of the general theory, with introduction to all the mathematical tools needed: Maxwell, analytical geometry, non-Euclidean geometry, tensor calculus, etc. Basis is classical space-time, before absorption of relativity. Partial contents: Euclidean space, mathematical form, metrical continuum, relativity of time and space, general theory. 15 diagrams. Bibliography. New preface for this edition. xviii + 330pp. 5⅜ x 8.
S267 Paperbound **$2.25**

ATOMIC SPECTRA AND ATOMIC STRUCTURE, G. Herzberg. Excellent general survey for chemists, physicists specializing in other fields. Partial contents: simplest line spectra and elements of atomic theory, building-up principle and periodic system of elements, hyperfine structure of spectral lines, some experiments and applications. Bibliography. 80 figures. Index. xii + 257pp. 5⅜ x 8.
S115 Paperbound **$2.00**

SELECTED PAPERS ON QUANTUM ELECTRODYNAMICS, edited by **J. Schwinger.** Facsimiles of papers which established quantum electrodynamics, from initial successes through today's position as part of the larger theory of elementary particles. First book publication in any language of these collected papers of Bethe, Bloch, Dirac, Dyson, Fermi, Feynman, Heisenberg, Kusch, Lamb, Oppenheimer, Pauli, Schwinger, Tomonoga, Weisskopf, Wigner, etc. 34 papers in all, 29 in English, 1 in French, 3 in German, 1 in Italian. Preface and historical commentary by the editor, xvii + 423pp. 6⅛ x 9¼. S444 Paperbound **$2.75**

THE FUNDAMENTAL PRINCIPLES OF QUANTUM MECHANICS, WITH ELEMENTARY APPLICATIONS, **E. C. Kemble.** An inductive presentation, for the graduate student or specialist in some other branch of physics. Assumes some acquaintance with advanced math; apparatus necessary beyond differential equations and advanced calculus is developed as needed. Although a general exposition of principles, hundreds of individual problems are fully treated, with applications of theory being interwoven with development of the mathematical structure. The author is the Professor of Physics at Harvard Univ. "This excellent book would be of great value to every student . . . a rigorous and detailed mathematical discussion of all of the principal quantum-mechanical methods . . . has succeeded in keeping his presentations clear and understandable," Dr. Linus Pauling, J. of the American Chemical Society. Appendices: calculus of variations, math. notes, etc. Indexes. 611pp. 5⅜ x 8. S472 Paperbound **$3.00**

QUANTUM MECHANICS, H. A. Kramers. A superb, up-to-date exposition, covering the most important concepts of quantum theory in exceptionally lucid fashion. 1st half of book shows how the classical mechanics of point particles can be generalized into a consistent quantum mechanics. These 5 chapters constitute a thorough introduction to the foundations of quantum theory. Part II deals with those extensions needed for the application of the theory to problems of atomic and molecular structure. Covers electron spin, the Exclusion Principle, electromagnetic radiation, etc. "This is a book that all who study quantum theory will want to read," J. Polkinghorne, PHYSICS TODAY. Translated by D. ter Haar. Prefaces, introduction. Glossary of symbols. 14 figures. Index. xvi + 496pp. 5⅜ x 8⅜. S1150 Paperbound **$2.75**

THE THEORY AND THE PROPERTIES OF METALS AND ALLOYS, N. F. Mott, H. Jones. Quantum methods used to develop mathematical models which show interrelationship of basic chemical phenomena with crystal structure, magnetic susceptibility, electrical, optical properties. Examines thermal properties of crystal lattice, electron motion in applied field, cohesion, electrical resistance, noble metals, para-, dia-, and ferromagnetism, etc. "Exposition . . . clear . . . mathematical treatment . . . simple," Nature. 138 figures. Bibliography. Index. xiii + 320pp. 5⅜ x 8. S456 Paperbound **$2.00**

FOUNDATIONS OF NUCLEAR PHYSICS, edited by **R. T. Beyer.** 13 of the most important papers on nuclear physics reproduced in facsimile in the original languages of their authors: the papers most often cited in footnotes, bibliographies. Anderson, Curie, Joliot, Chadwick, Fermi, Lawrence, Cockcroft, Hahn, Yukawa. UNPARALLELED BIBLIOGRAPHY. 122 double-columned pages, over 4,000 articles, books, classified. 57 figures. 288pp. 6⅛ x 9¼. S19 Paperbound **$2.00**

MESON PHYSICS, R. E. Marshak. Traces the basic theory, and explicitly presents results of experiments with particular emphasis on theoretical significance. Phenomena involving mesons as virtual transitions are avoided, eliminating some of the least satisfactory predictions of meson theory. Includes production and study of π mesons at nonrelativistic nucleon energies, contrasts between π and μ mesons, phenomena associated with nuclear interaction of π mesons, etc. Presents early evidence for new classes of particles and indicates theoretical difficulties created by discovery of heavy mesons and hyperons. Name and subject indices. Unabridged reprint. viii + 378pp. 5⅜ x 8. S500 Paperbound **$1.95**

Prices subject to change without notice.

Dover publishes books on art, music, philosophy, literature, languages, history, social sciences, psychology, handcrafts, orientalia, puzzles and entertainments, chess, pets and gardens, books explaining science, intermediate and higher mathematics, mathematical physics, engineering, biological sciences, earth sciences, classics of science, etc. Write to:

Dept. catrr.
Dover Publications, Inc.
180 Varick Street, N.Y. 14, N.Y.